FABLIAUX

FABLIAUX

Ribald Tales from the Old French

Translated, with Notes and Afterword, by

Robert Hellman and *Richard O'Gorman*

Illustrated by *Ashley Bryan*

Thomas Y. Crowell Company

New York, Established 1834

CONTENTS

FABLIAUX

THE WIFE OF ORLEANS
&
LA BORGOISE D'ORLIENS

Let me tell you that very courtly tale of a burgher's wife; she was born and raised in Orleans, and her husband was born in Amiens. He was a property owner, rich beyond measure, his purse bulging with the profits of trade and usury. He knew all the twists and turns of making money, and once he had it in his fist he never let it go.

One day into this town of Orleans there came four young

scholars with their wallets slung about their necks. These scholars were fat and sleek, for they took their bellies seriously and stuffed themselves well. And they soon found great favor and good lodging in that city.

One of them, a fellow of some breeding, took to frequenting a burgher's house; and, since he was an agreeable and elegant young man, not puffed up with pride, the young wife soon took a liking to him and was very pleased with his company. But it happened after a while, what with one thing and another, that the burgher grew somewhat suspicious of their friendship and made up his mind that, if he could do something about it, he would soon put this young man to the test. So one day he secretly he took aside a young niece of his, who lived in his house and whom he had raised, and promised her a new dress if she would play the spy for him and tell him truthfully whatever she could find out in this matter.

Now the young scholar had pleaded his case so well that the burgher's wife agreed to grant him her favors. But the niece, who had her ear to the door, heard all their plans and ran immediately to the burgher to tell him everything: how his wife had promised the young man that as soon as her husband was away on one of his journeys she would send for him to come to the garden, where she would meet him at the two locked gates when night had fallen.

The burgher was overjoyed to hear this news, and he went at once to his wife and said: "My wife, I have to go on a journey to further my affairs. Be a good wife in all things, my dear, and take good care of our house, for I do not know when I shall return."

"Husband," she said, "that I will."

The burgher then gave instructions to his carters and said that he would ride out and lodge some three leagues from the town so as to get his journey under way. The good wife, unaware of her husband's ruse, sent for the young scholar to tell him of their luck. But the sly burgher, having lodged his servants at an inn, rode back and came to the garden gate himself as day was changing to night.

All secretly the wife met him there and opened the gate for him and took him in her arms, thinking that he was her lover; but she was disappointed in her expectations. "How welcome you are!" she said to him, and the burgher, that his voice might not betray him, returned her greeting softly. Together then they walked through the garden, but he kept his head bowed very low. The wife, however, bending over a little, caught a glimpse under his hood; also, she recognized him and knew at once that she had been betrayed and that her husband had set a trap for her.

No sooner had she understood this than she began to think how best she might take her husband in his own trap. For you must know that in these matters women have more eyes than Argus, and wise men have been fooled by their devices ever since the days of Abel.

"My lord," she said, "it is a great delight to me to have you here and to embrace you, and if only you will be discreet in this affair I shall give you money enough to get your possessions out of pawn. Then let us go in quickly and I shall hide you secretly in a loft nearby, to which I have the key. There you must wait for me silently until the servants have eaten, and when all have gone to bed, I shall come and bring you to my bed. No one will ever find out about our arrangement."

"Lady," said the burgher, "you have spoken well." Lord! how little he knew what she was thinking and plotting! As they say: the mule driver thinks he knows where he's going, but the mules have their own idea. Soon the burgher will not be so well lodged.

As for his wife, no sooner had she locked him up in the loft from which he could not escape than she ran back to the garden, where at the gate she found her lover waiting. Him she took in her arms and hugged and kissed. He had a much better time of it, I think, than did the burgher, who for a long time was left alone to roost in his loft.

Then the burgher's wife and the scholar went quickly through the garden and into the house. There the lady led her lover into her chamber where the bedsheets were spread on the bed, and she let him in under the covers and lay down beside him. Soon he was at that game which the God of Love makes all lovers play, and both the wife and the scholar took such pleasure in it that they would not have given a penny for all the other games in the world.

And when they had played together for a long time and had kissed and hugged to their hearts' content, she got up and said: "My dear, stay here for a little while and wait for me, for I must go to see to the dinner for my household. Then we shall have our supper quietly, just you and I alone, this very night." "Lady," he said, "I am at your orders."

Then the burgher's wife softly left him and went into the hall, where she did all in her power to please her retainers. When the meal was prepared, they sat down and ate and drank their fill. And when they had finished, their lady called them all together and, still at table, spoke to them shrewdly. There were among them two of the burgher's nephews, a lad who carried the water, three chambermaids, the burgher's niece, two valets, and one sturdy beggar.

"Good friends," she said, "as God may bless you, listen to what I have to say. You must have seen hanging about the house a young scholar who has been plaguing me for a long time with his talk of love and who will not leave me in peace. God knows, I have tried thirty different ways to put him off, but when I saw that he would not let me alone, I promised him at last that I would do what he wanted as soon as my husband had gone on a journey.

"Well, my lord is now away—may God watch over him!— and that young man who has been bothering me every day has kept me to our bargain and has come at the appointed time. He is waiting for me now up there in the loft. Now, I will give you each a measure of the finest wine in the house if you will agree to avenge me on him. Go up to the loft, take that fellow, stretch him on the ground, and give him a good cudgeling. Let him have plenty of rough blows, so that never again will he take it into his head to go courting an honest woman."

When her people had heard what she had to say, they all jumped to their feet; not one remained behind. One grabbed a cudgel, another a club, a third a pestle, a thick heavy one. The wife gave them the key to the loft, and off they went.

"Go up there and take hold of him," the wife called after them, "and let it take a good counter to number the blows!"

"By God, little sir scholar," they said when they got there, "we'll teach you some manners!"

One of them threw him to the ground and seized him by the throat, twisting his hood so tight about him that he could not let out a word. Then they set about beating him, and they were not the least bit stingy in the allowance of thwacks and cuffs they gave him. They took the rust off his coat of mail— he couldn't have got a better cleaning for a thousand marks. His two nephews, when they had roasted him well with their cudgels on one side, turned him over and worked on the other. It was no use his crying for mercy. And when they were done with him they dragged him out like a dead dog and threw him on a dung heap.

They then went back into the house, where they found a great plenty of wine, both white and red, the finest in the house, and they sat and drank like kings. But the wife took cakes and wine to her chamber and white linen napkins and a great wax candle; and she and her lover passed the whole night together until the day broke. When he left her arms, so well had he made love that she gave him a present of ten marks and begged him to come again as often as he could.

As for the burgher lying on the dung heap, he got up as best he could and made his way to the place where he had left his gear. When his servants saw him in that sad condition, all bruised and battered, they were much grieved and astonished and asked the poor man how he felt. "Bad," he said, "bad! Carry me back to my house and ask me nothing more." And so his servants without further delay picked him up and carried him away. Despite his pain, however, the burgher was not cast down, but was much cheered by the idea that he had such a loyal wife. Really he didn't care a farthing for all his pain, and he thought that if only he could recover from his wounds he would always love and cherish his good woman.

When he returned home, his wife, seeing him so wretched, came and made him a bath with healing herbs steeped in it to cure him of his hurt, and she asked him what had happened to him. "Wife," he said, "I have come through great danger, and certain wicked people that I met have broken my bones." The servants came to his bedside too and told him how they fixed the young scholar: how their mistress had handed him over to them and how roughly they had handled him. "I swear," he said, "she behaved like a wise and virtuous woman."

After that, in all his life, the burgher never found fault with his wife nor mistrusted her. And she never gave up making love to her young scholar until he returned to his own country.

Or vous dirai d'une borgoise
Une aventure assez cortoise;
Nee et norrie fu d'Orliens,
Et ses sires fu nez d'Amiens,
Riches mananz a desmesure.
De marcheandise et d'usure
Savoit toz les tors et les poins,
Et ce que il tenoit aus poins
Estoit bien fermement tenu.
En la vile furent venu
Quatre noviaus clers escoliers,
Lor sas portent comme coliers.
Li clerc estoient gros et gras,
Quar molt menjoient bien, sanz gas.
En la vile erent molt proisié
Ou il estoient herbregié.
Un en i ot de grant ponois
Qui molt hantoit chiés un borgois,
Sel tenoit on molt a cortois;
N'ert plains d'orgueil ne de bufois.
Et a la dame vraiement
Plesoit molt son acointement.
Et tant vint et tant i ala
Que li borgois se propenssa,
Fust par samblant ou par parole,

Que il le metroit a escole,
S'il en pooit en leu venir
Que a ce le peüst tenir.
Leenz ot une seue niece
Qu'il ot norrie molt grant piece;
Priveement a soi l'apele,
Se li promet une cotele
Mes qu'el soit de cele oevre espie
Et que la verité l'en die.
Et l'escolier a tant proié
La borgoise par amistié
Que sa volenté li otroie.
Et la meschine toute voie
Fu en escout tant qu'ele oï
Comme il orent lor plet basti.
Au borgois en vient maintenant
Et li conte le couvenant;
Et li couvenanz tels estoit
Que la dame le manderoit
Quant ses sires seroit errez;
Lors venist aus deus huis serrez
Du vergier qu'el li enseigna,
Et el seroit contre lui la
Quant il seroit bien anuitié.
Li borgois l'ot, molt fu haitié;
A sa fame maintenant vient:
"Dame, fet il, il me covient
Aler en ma marcheandie.
Gardez l'ostel, ma chiere amie,
Si com preude fame doit fere.
Je ne sai rien de mon repere."
"Sire, fet ele, volentiers."

Cil atorna les charretiers
Et dist qu'il s'iroit herbregier,
Por ses jornees avancier,
Jusqu'a trois liues de la vile.
La dame ne sot pas la guile,
Si fist au clerc l'uevre savoir.
Cil qui les cuida decevoir
Fist sa gent aler herbregier
Et il vint a l'uis du vergier,
Quar la nuit fu au jor meslee.
Et la dame tout a celee
Vint encontre, l'uis li ouvri,
Entre ses braz le recueilli,
Qu'el cuide que son ami soit;
Mes experance la deçoit.
"Bien soiez vous, dist el, venuz."
Cil s'est de haut parler tenuz,
Se li rent ses saluz en bas.
Par le vergier s'en vont le pas,
Mes il tint molt la chiere encline;
Et la borgoise un pou s'acline,
Par souz le chaperon l'esgarde,
De trahison se done garde,
Si connut bien et aperçoit;
C'est son mari qui la deçoit!
Quant el le prist a aperçoivre,
Si repensse de lui deçoivre.
Fame a trestout passé Argu,
Par lor engin sont deceü
Li sage des le tens Abel.
"Sire, fet ele, molt m'est bel
Que tenir vous puis et avoir;

Je vous donrai de mon avoir,
Dont vous porrez voz gages trere,
Se vous celez bien cest afere.
Or alons ça tout belement;
Je vous metrai priveement
En un solier dont j'ai la clef;
Iluec m'atendrez tout souef
Tant que noz genz avront mengié;
Et quant trestuit seront couchié,
Je vous menrai souz ma cortine;
Ja nus ne savra la couvine."
"Dame, fet il, bien avez dit."
Dieus! comme il savoit or petit
De ce qu'ele pensse et porpensse;
Li asniers une chose pensse
Et li asnes pensse tout el.
Tost avra il mauvés ostel,
Quar quant la dame enfermé l'ot
El solier, dont issir ne pot,
A l'uis del vergier retorna,
Son ami prist qu'ele trova,
Si l'enbrace et acole et baise.
Molt est, je cuit, a meillor aise
Li secons que le premerain.
La dame lessa le vilain
Longuement ou solier jouchier.
Tost ont trespassé le vergier
Tant qu'en la chambre sont venu
Ou li drap furent portendu.
La dame son ami amaine
Jusqu'en la chambre le demaine,
Si l'a souz le couvertoir mis.
Et cil s'est tantost entremis

Du geu que Amors li commande,
Qu'il ne prisast une alemande
Toz les autres, se cil n'i fust,
Ne cele gre ne l'en seüst.
Longuement se sont envoisié;
Quant ont acolé et baisié,
   "Amis, fet ele, or remaindrez
Un petit et si m'atendrez,
Quar je m'en irai la dedenz
Por fere mengier cele gent;
Et nous souperons, vous et moi,
Encore anuit tout a recoi."
"Dame, a vostre commandement."
Cele s'en part molt belement,
Vint en la sale a sa mesnie,
A son pooir la fet haitie.
Quant li mengiers fu atornez,
Menjüent et boivent assez.
Et quant orent mengié trestuit,
Ainz qu'il fussent desrengié tuit,
La dame apele sa mesnie,
Si parole comme enseignie.
Deus neveus au seignor i ot
Et un garz qui eve aportoit,
Et chamberieres i ot trois,
Si i fu la niece au borgois,
Deus pautoniers et un ribaut.
"Seignor, fet el, se Dieus vous saut,
Entendez ore ma reson:
Vous avez en ceste meson
Veü ceenz un clerc venir
Qui ne me lest en pes garir.
Requise m'a d'amors lonc tens;

Je l'en ai fet trente desfens.
Quant je vi que je n'i garroie,
Je li promis que je feroie
Tout son plesir et tout son gre
Quant mon seignor seroit erré.
Or est errez, Dieus le conduie!
Et cil qui chascun jor m'anuie
A molt bien couvenant tenu.
Or est a son terme venu;
Lasus m'atent en ce perrin.
Je vous donrai du meillor vin
Qui soit ceenz une galoie
Par couvant que vengie en soie.
En ce solier a lui alez
Et de bastons bien le batez
Encontre terre et en estant;
Des orbes cops li donez tant
Que jamés jor ne li en chaille
De prïer fame qui rien vaille."

    Quant la mesnie l'uevre entent,
Tuit saillent sus, nus n'i atent;
L'un prent baston, l'autre tiné,
L'autre pestel gros et mollé.
La borgoise la clef lor baille;
"Qui toz les cops meïst en taille
A bon conteor le tenisse.
Ne soufrez pas que il en isse,
Ainz l'acueilliez el solier haut!"
"Par Dieu, font il, sire clercgaut,
Vous serez ja desciplinez!"
Li uns l'a a terre aclinez
Et par la gorge le saisi;

Par le chaperon l'estraint si
Que il ne puet nul mot soner.
Puis l'en acueillent a doner;
De batre ne sont mie eschars.
S'il en eüst doné mil mars,
N'eüst mieus son hauberc roulé.
Par maintes foiz se sont mollé
Por bien ferir ses deus nevous,
Primes desus et puis desous;
Merci crïer ne li vaut rien.
Hors le traient comme un mort chien,
Si l'ont sor un fumier flati;
En la meson sont reverti.
De bons vins orent a foison,
Toz des meillors de la meson,
Et des blans et des auvernois,
Autant com se il fussent rois.
Et la dame ot gastiaus et vin
Et blanche toaille de lin
Et grosse chandoile de cire,
Si tient a son ami concile
Toute la nuit dusques au jor.
Au departir si fist amor
Que vaillant dis mars li dona
Et de revenir li prïa
Toutes les foiz que il porroit.
Et cil qui el fumier gisoit
Si se remua comme il pot,
Et vait la ou son harnois ot.
Quant ses genz si batu le virent,
Duel orent grant, si s'esbahirent.
Enquis li ont comment ce vait:

"Malement, ce dist il, me vait;
A mon ostel m'en reportez
Et plus rien ne me demandez."
Tout maintenant l'ont levé sus,
Onques n'i atendirent plus.
Mes ce l'a molt reconforté
Et mis hors de mauvés penssé
Qu'il sent sa fame a si loial;
Un oef ne prise tout son mal
Et pensse, s'il en puet garir,
Molt la voudra toz jors chierir.

A son ostel est revenu.
Et quant la dame l'a veü,
De bones herbes li fist baing,
Tout le gari de son mehaing.
Demande lui com il avint:
"Dame, fet il, il me covint
Par un destroit peril passer
Ou l'en me fist des os quasser."
Cil de la meson li conterent
Du clercgaut, comme il l'atornerent,
Comment la dame lor livra.
"Par mon chief, el s'en delivra
Com preude fame et comme sage."
Onques puis en tout son eage
Ne la blasma ne ne mescrut;
N'onques cele ne se recrut
De son ami amer toz dis
Tant qu'il ala en son païs.

Explicit de la Borgoise d'Orliens

"La Borgoise d'Orliens" is preserved in three manuscripts which differ from one another in detail and arrangement but clearly derive from the same original composition. The tale dates from the second half of the thirteenth century and in all probability was written in the dialect of Normandy, as certain linguistic features would seem to indicate. Folklorists generally designate its main theme as *the false fidelity test*, although traditionally it is known by the much more savory name, *the cuckold beaten and content*.

According to the medievalist Schofield, the plot of "The Wife of Orleans" stems ultimately from an actual event related by the Saxon historian Bruno in his *De Bello Saxonico* (*The Saxon War*; 1082), another account of which is found in the twelfth-century *Annales Palidenses* (*Palace Annals*). But though the resemblances are striking, the intrigue is such a commonplace one that no specific source need be cited. Certainly this plot owes little or nothing to Eastern or folk narrative, but seems, like so many clever triangle stories, to have sprung full-grown from the fertile mind of the jongleur or popular storyteller and spread rapidly to many parts of Europe in the early Middle Ages. "The Wife of Orleans" represents perhaps its first appearance in literary form.

Thereafter the story proliferated with great vitality and with varying degrees of modification. It would be difficult to determine the relationship among the various versions of the tale; it is not even certain that the later poets who drew on the story used one of the extant versions. But, although the theme of the finished tale is, relatively speaking, a new composition, certain of its elements are very ancient indeed. In both Eastern and medieval stories, for instance, there are many analogues of the feigned journey with which a husband tests the fidelity of his wife.

By the end of the thirteenth century there appeared a second fabliau on the same theme: "Un Chivalier et Sa Dame et un Clerk" ("A Knight and His Wife and a Cleric"), written in England by an Anglo-Norman poet. This story is devoid of the brutality and cynicism of "The Wife," and is, in its more elevated tone and its concern with character development, reminiscent of the courtly romance. In the same century the story also turns up in the Catalan *Castia Gilos* (*School for the Jealous*), a narrative poem of considerable merit written by the troubadour Raimon Vidal. Raimon's story, set at the court of Aragon, differs from the usual version in that the wife is faithful until the husband's trick drives her into the arms of her lover. As part of a longer narrative, a similar account was also incorporated into the late-medieval epic *Baudouin de Sebourc*.

But it was the art of Boccaccio which, in the seventh novel of the seventh day of the *Decameron,* immortalized the beaten cuckold and provided the model for La Fontaine, who in his *Contes* (*Tales*) brought the story back to France as "Le Cocu Battu et Content" ("The Cuckold Beaten and Content"). In these two versions the lover has become the husband's trusted valet, and the ruse that backfires serves not only to exonerate the wife, but also to convince the husband of the fidelity of his valet. In imitation of Boccaccio two other Italian versions followed: the second novel of the third day in *Il Pecorone* (*The Dolt;* pub. 1558) by Ser Giovanni (fl. 1380) and the first novel of the fourth day in Sansovino's *Cento Novelle Scelte* (*A Hundred Select Tales;* 1556). In Spanish it turns up as the sixty-ninth tale of the *Sobremesa* (*After-Dinner Tales;* 1563) of Timoneda, and in German as the "Frauenbeständigkeit" ("The Constancy of Woman") in Von der Hagen's *Gesammtabenteuer* (*Collected Tales;* 1850). Finally, an English version was printed by John Rastell in 1526 as "Of the Wife that Made Her Husband Go Sit in the Arbor While Her 'Prentice Lay with Her in Bed," Tale Three of *A Hundred Merry Tales* (ed. P. M. Zall; Lincoln, Nebraska, 1963; pp. 65–67).

Edition: Richard O'Gorman, *La Bourgeoise d'Orléans* (St. Louis, Washington University, 1957).

THE SNOW BABY

Once upon a time there was a merchant, an industrious fellow, a good money-maker, who often went abroad into divers countries to find suitable markets for his goods and so never ceased to pile up wealth. One day, the tale goes on, he left his wife and went off on a long journey. He was gone for two whole years; and while he was away his wife, with the help of a young man she knew, got herself pregnant. Love, which lies always in wait, had so warmed the two of them that at last they lay together. And their work was not without wages. For, as I say, the wife grew big and gave birth to a son.

When the merchant returned, he asked his wife, as any clever man would, how she had managed to give birth to a child in his absence. His wife replied: "Husband, once when I was looking out for you up there on the high balcony, all sad and sorrowful at your delay, I chanced to look up at the sky, and it being winter and the snow falling heavily, a little snow fell into my mouth. Before I was aware of it I swallowed it, and it was so sweet that from the little I swallowed I conceived this beautiful child. And this happened just as I have told it."

When he had heard her story, the good man said to his wife: "My wife, this really is good luck; from now on I shall know that God loves me, thanks be to Him! For He has given me this fine heir, who, God willing, will be a good man when he grows up." After that he said no more about the matter, but in his heart he did not believe her story.

The child sucked well at the breast and grew tall and stout. But the merchant spent his days brooding about the strange circumstances of his birth and plotting how to get rid of him. At last, when the boy was fifteen years old, the merchant, who still harbored his grudge, went to his wife and said: "Wife, do not be unhappy, but tomorrow, without delay, I must be off on another journey. So pack my clothes, for I must get up early in the morning. And lay out your son's clothes, because I intend to take him with me tomorrow. Do you want to know why? I'll tell you without your asking. It is so that he can learn the business while he is still young. You must know that if a man is to be good at his trade he must put his heart in it and work hard at it before he is past his prime."

"Husband," his wife said, "if it pleased you I would prefer that my son not go. But, since it is your wish, there is nothing I can say against it. Tomorrow you must go on your way; and I pray that God, who lives in heaven, will watch over you and give you good fortune and bring my son home safe and sound."

The following morning the merchant got up and made himself ready. He was not worried about his business affairs, for everything was going well. But his wife was not at all pleased to see her son leave, perhaps never to return to her.

So the merchant took the boy with him and brought him down through Lombardy. I won't say much about their trip, except that they passed through many countries until they came to Genoa, where they put up at an inn. There the merchant sold the boy to a man who took him to Alexandria to sell him on the slave market. When he had done this and settled his other business, without further ado he set off for home, passing through many countries before he reached his own house.

But when he got there and his wife saw that he had not brought back her son, she was so overcome with grief that she fainted again and again. At last, when she had come to herself, she begged him to tell her, for the love of God, what had become of her son.

The merchant, who had a smooth tongue, was only too glad to tell her. "Wife," he said, "everyone must resign himself to the ills of this world. Giving way to grief will do no good. Listen and I will tell you what happened. It was on a hot summer's day just about noon in the country where we were traveling, when I and your son went for a walk on a very high hill where the rays of the sun, which were very bright and burning hot, fell full on our heads. Alas, that walk cost us dear! For the boy, exposed to the full heat of the sun, all at once melted away. And it is no wonder that he did, for as we know he was made of snow."

The merchant's wife understood then that her husband

had tricked her and turned her own weapon on her. The husband was well avenged on her for her foul betrayal, both in word and in deed. And surely no one can blame him for what he did or say that he wronged his wife. For all her wrongs came only to this: that she had to drink what she herself had brewed.

The markedly brutal and cynical tale "L'Enfant Qui Fu Remis au Soleil," preserved in a single manuscript, is the oldest literary version of a theme which enjoyed wide popularity in the folklore of many countries and which still is alive today in the Scandinavian countries and in France. From this anonymous fabliau derive Tale XIX of the *Cent Nouvelles Nouvelles* (*The Hundred New Tales;* 1462); a *conte* of Grécourt, and Tale XLVII of Von der Hagen's *Gesammtabenteuer* (*Collected Tales;* 1850). But it was in Italy that the story attained its greatest popularity. It is found in Agnolo Firenzuola's *Discorso degli animali* (*Discourses of the Animals;* 1552); in the *Novelle* of Doni (1513–1574) as Tale XLI; in Celio Malespini's *Ducento Novelle* (*Two Hundred Tales;* 1609), I, XXXVIII; in the *Novelle* (*Tales*) of Giovanni Sercambi (1347–1424), XC; and in Sansovino's *Cento Novelle Scelte* (*A Hundred Select Tales;* 1556), IX, V.

The nucleus of the tale—the motif of the child conceived by swallowing an object usually possessing magic qualities—preserves, in all probability, a superstition of long standing. But the humorous turn given to the story by making the object a snowflake and causing the child so conceived to melt is to be considered, according to the medievalist Joseph Bédier, simply a monkish joke. Many similar anecdotes are, in fact, preserved in medieval Latin versions written in monasteries. Compare, for instance, the following verses found in a Trinity College manuscript:

De nive conceptum quem mater adultera fingit
Sponsus eum vendens liquefactum sole refingit.
(What an adulterous mother claims was conceived by snow
Her merchant husband maintains was turned to liquid by the sun.)

Similarly, a fifteenth-century play contains the following dialogue between two accusers of the Virgin Mary:

—— My word, I imagine that the woman was sleeping once without a cover and it was snowing, and a snowflake having slipped into her mouth, the child was conceived in her womb.

—— Take care, then, woman. It is well known that a child born under such circumstances returns to a liquid state if the sun shines on him.

Edition: Montaiglon-Raynaud, I, 162.

THE BEATEN PATH

by Jean de Condé

It is not wise to make fun of others or to say things that grieve people or make them ashamed. Many cases may be cited to prove this. Nor is it good to make earnest of game; for it is truly said that in joking one must expect tit for tat. Anyone who is insulted or made a butt of will take his revenge if he gets the chance; and whoever takes to mocking others will find that his joke rebounds on his own head. I shall tell you a story to demonstrate this, a true story—I would never lie—just as it was told to me.

A tournament was to be held midway between Péronne and Atiés, and the knights of those parts were sojourning there while waiting for it to begin. One day they held a *fête galante* at which were present ladies and damsels of great beauty and elegance. They played at many games, and at last they chose a queen so that they might play the game called The King Who Does Not Lie. This queen was very clever at the game and undertook to give orders and ask questions, for she was graceful and well spoken and lovely and charming in manner.

She asked many questions and had everything her own way until she came to a knight, a very courteous and eloquent gentleman, who had loved her and who would have taken her for his wife if she had consented; but he did not have the look of a man who could please his mistress when he held her naked in his arms. For his beard was not very thick; indeed, it was little more than the kind of fuzz that ladies have in certain places. "Sir," the queen said to him, "tell me a little of your affairs. Did you ever have any children?" "Lady," he said, "I can boast of none, for I never had any to my knowledge." "My lord," she said, "I do not doubt your word for a moment, and I believe I am not alone in that. For it is easy to judge from the state of the hay whether the pitchfork is any good."

After that nothing more was said of the matter, and she went on to question someone else and spoke of other things. But all those who were listening remarked her words and smiled. As for the knight, he took no joy in what he heard; he was dumbfounded and didn't say a word.

And when the game had gone on long enough for the queen to make the complete round of questions, then everyone in his turn put questions to her, as is the custom. She was subtle and witty and answered each one cleverly, without taking thought or hesitating. When the knight's turn came, he remembered her jeer and wanted his revenge. So at once he said to her: "Lady, answer me without deceit. Is there hair between your legs?" "In faith," said the damsel, "here's a pretty question and one very much to the point. Know then that there is none at all." At which he said to her in full agreement: "Indeed I do believe you, for grass does not grow on a well-beaten path."

They who heard this proverb laughed so loud at the cunning question that the queen was all ashamed—she who only a while ago had been so eager to say things and ask questions that would make the company laugh. Her heart was so dismayed that all good spirits left her, she who before was joyful and gay and full of merriment. The knight could not have taken his revenge at more polished ease. He had no wish to insult her, but only to bring her up short and show her what was in his mind, as she had shown him what was in hers.

For there was never an earthly woman who could love a man whom she had given the bad name of a poor workman in bed, unfit for amorous delights, and whom she had made fun of on that score. Know indeed that, as the caponed cock is poorly received by the hens, so the man reputed to be a poor workman is scorned by the women. For women might as well be nuns when such a man is about, as are hens in the company of a capon.

The knight, who well knew what reputation he had, was cut to the heart by her mockery and wanted his revenge. It is very possible that he knew or suspected something about her affairs, something he had learned in the course of their marriage negotiations, when perhaps she had bared her heart to him. If she had kept quiet, he would never have reminded her of such a thing.

You who hear this tale may understand that such earnest jokes are worth nothing; few of them turn out well, and then only by chance, but most of them turn out badly. I know of few which have succeeded. I have put into new rhyme this story I have told. May God preserve those who have listened to it. Amen. Here ends my tale. May God grant you all a good end!

The author of "Le Sentier Battu," "The Petticoat," and "The Priest's Breeches" is usually considered the last practitioner of the fabliau genre. Jean de Condé, whose literary activity can be dated between 1313 and about 1340, was the son of a famous court minstrel of Picardy, Baudouin de Condé. Like his father, Jean served for many years in the capacity of court poet to the counts of Flanders and Hainaut, provinces which are today in Belgium. He excelled in all the minor genres, writing exclusively for the court circles at a time when Flemish tastes were beginning to dominate literary production. His death in 1346 brought to a close the period of the Old French fabliau.

The three fabliaux translated here are among the five preserved in the work of Jean de Condé; although they were composed at the beginning of the Middle French period, they reflect the preoccupation with intrigue and the spirit of the classical era of the fabliau some hundred years earlier. "The Beaten Path" is not a tale in the usual sense of the word, but a simple anecdote which revolves around the salacious equivocations produced by two proverbs—a neat repartee, despite the author's inclination to sententiousness. The story seems to have had no antecedents and did not produce any imitations in other literatures. Perhaps it may derive from an actual event, for it describes a well-known party game, King and Queen. This game was proscribed by the Council of Worcester in 1240 because of the lascivious spirit which it all too often engendered, as it does in the fabliau, where two noble young people hurl refined insults at each other.

Edition: August Scheler, *Dits et Contes de Baudouin de Condé et de Son Fils Jean de Condé*. 3 vols. (Brussels, 1866). III, 299–303.

BRUNAIN, THE PRIEST'S COW

by Jean Bodel

I tell about a peasant and his wife, who, one day, on the feast of Our Lady, went to church to pray. Before mass the priest went to the pulpit to preach a sermon. And he said that, if one looked at things reasonably, it was good to give for the sake of God; for he who had given from his heart, God would return him twice as much.

"Listen to what our priest has promised, sweet sister," said the peasant, "that he who gives willingly for the love of God, God will increase his wealth. We cannot find a better use for our cow, if it please you, than to give her to the priest for God's sake. Besides, she gives little milk." "Husband," said his wife, "if that's the way it is, I am perfectly willing to let him have her."

The peasant went into his barn, took the cow by the halter, and went to present her to the priest, who was a wise and cunning man. "Good sir," said the peasant, approaching him with joined hands, "for the love of God, I give you Blerain." He placed the halter in his hand and swore that he had no other goods. "Friend, you have acted wisely," said the priest, Don Constant, who was always ready to take. "Now go away. You have done your errand well. If all my parishioners were as well behaved as you are, I would have plenty of cattle."

The peasant left the priest, and the latter at once gave orders that Blerain be tied with Brunain, his own big cow, in order to tame her. The priest's clerk took the cow into the garden, where he found the priest's cow, and he tied them both together. The priest's cow lowered her head because she wanted to graze, but Blerain wouldn't stand for that. Instead, she pulled so hard on the lead rope that she dragged Brunain out of the garden. She led her past houses and through hemp fields and meadows, until she got back to her own place together with the priest's cow, who was very much chagrined to be led so.

When the peasant saw her, his heart was full of joy. "Ah!" he said, "sweet sister, truly God is a good doubler; for here Blerain has come back and she's bringing a big brown cow with her. Now we have two for one. Our barn will be small."

This fabliau is a lesson to show that he is a fool who does not give freely; for he who does so receives the goods which God bestows, but not he who hides and hoards. And it is plain that no man may increase his wealth without great luck. By great luck the peasant got two cows, while the priest had none. Some think they are advancing when they are losing ground.

The author of "Brunain, la Vache au Prestre" is Jean Bodel of Arras, well known at the turn of the thirteenth century as the perfect example of the professional man of letters. He is the first author of authentic fabliaux whose name is known. If he was not the originator of the genre, he nonetheless put his distinctive stamp on it, fixed its form, and perhaps was instrumental in popularizing it. But it was not only in the fabliaux that Jean Bodel excelled, for he was one of the most prolific authors of his age and composed in most of the traditional literary forms. He has left a collection of lyric poetry, an epic poem entitled *La Chanson des Saisnes* (*The Song of the Saxons*), and one of the finest dramas in Old French, *Le Jeu de Saint Nicolas* (*The Play of Saint Nicolas*). Few facts about his life are known. A native of Arras in Picardy, he was a professional poet. He was dedicated to the Christian cause in its struggle with Islam, but leprosy, which he contracted in 1202, prevented him from participating in the Fourth Crusade. Withdrawing from the world, he entered an institution for lepers near Arras, where he died during the winter of 1209–1210.

The two fabliaux translated here are among eight known to have been composed by Jean Bodel. "Brunain, the Priest's Cow" belongs to a group of fabliaux termed *"fabliaux simplistes,"* that is, those whose comical vein is exceedingly superficial. Although facile, the humor is nonetheless wholesome, and the portrait of the peasant couple most sympathetic. The priest is a portrayal of a type common in the fabliaux, the avaricious clergy. The entire plot turns about the simplest of points—the literal interpretation of a passage from scripture: he who gives willingly to God will be rewarded twofold. Although no theologian, the peasant possesses an earthy shrewdness which turns out to his advantage.

There is no known source for the tale, though the existence of several later versions, not taken from "Brunain," suggests that there was an older tale from which Jean Bodel drew the anecdote. Among these later versions are the *exemplum* No. 143 of Etienne de Bourbon (ca. 1191–ca. 1261) and a facetia, "Motti e Facezie" ("Maxims and Pleasantries"; 1515), attributed to the Italian priest Arlotto (1396–1484).

Edition: Johnston-Owen, pp. 34–35.

THE
BUTCHER
OF
ABBEVILLE

by Eustache d'Amiens

My lords, pay close attention to the wonderful tale I am going to tell, for I am sure you have never heard one like it; and also you must know that words which are not heard are wasted.

At Abbeville, then, there was a butcher, well liked by his neighbors, for he was not one of these malicious gossips but an honest man, trustworthy and well bred, a good workman in his craft; and when his poor neighbors were in need he was not stingy with them.

It happened once, a few days before the feast of All Hallows, that this butcher came to the market at Oisemont to buy beasts for the slaughter. But he found that he had made a useless journey; for the cattle were too dear, and the pigs were a bad breed, scrawny and worthless, altogether bad bargains.

He had certainly wasted a trip, for he didn't find a thing worth spending a penny on.

It was late in the day when the market closed and he started home, his cloak wrapped about him against the evening chill. And when he was halfway there, at the town of Bailleul, night overtook him, such a thick dark night that he decided to go no farther, but to try to find shelter in the town. For he was very much afraid that the gentlemen of the road might steal his money, which came to a tidy sum.

Hear now how he made out.

In the doorway of a house he spied a poor woman standing. He greeted her and said: "Is there any place in town where I can get lodging and some refreshment—at my own expense, you understand, for I never like to be a burden to others."

"My lord," the woman replied, "by God who made the world—an expression Mile, my husband, liked to use—there's no wine in this town except at the house of our priest, Gautier, who has two barrels in his cellar which he got at Noientel. He's always well stocked in wine. Go to him for lodging."

"My good woman," the butcher said, "I'll go there immediately. And God bless you!"

"Indeed, sir, may He bless you!"

He went on his way quickly as he could and came to the priest's house. There he found the owner seated on his threshold, a man all puffed up with pride. The butcher greeted him and said, "Dear sir, may God keep you. Will you for charity give me shelter? You will be doing me great honor if you will and great kindness."

"My good man," said the priest, "may God give you shelter. For, by Saint Herbert, no man not in orders may sleep in this house. There are plenty of people down there in the town who can give you lodging. Go up and down the streets until you find a place. For you may as well know that you can't lodge here. I have other guests, and anyway, it is not customary for a priest to let any low type sleep in his house."

"Low type! What are you saying, sir? Do you hold laymen in contempt?"

"Yes!" said the priest. "And I'm right to. Get away from my door! To my mind, your very presence here is an insult."

"But no, sir!" said the butcher. "If you give me shelter tonight when I have nowhere to go, it will be an act of charity. And I'm not stingy with my money; if you have anything to sell me, I'll be more than glad to buy it and very grateful to you for it. I don't want to put you to any expense."

"I'll sell you the right to run your head against this hard stone," said the priest. "By Saint Peter, you'll never lodge in my house!"

"May the devil lodge in it!" said the butcher. "You stupid priest, you're a rascal and a villain!" And with that, not wishing to continue the argument, he made off, full of rage and anger.

And listen now what happened to him.

When he had got a little way out of town, he came on an old abandoned house with a fallen roof, and in front of the house was a flock of sheep.

The butcher went up to the shepherd, who had kept many a cow and many a bull in his youth, and he said: "Shepherd, may God give you joy! Who do these sheep belong to?" "To my lord the priest," said the shepherd. "Good God!" said the butcher. "Can this be true?" And now listen to what he did!

Very slyly, when the shepherd wasn't looking, he made off

with one of the sheep. Oh, he stole a march on him, all right! He slung the beast over his shoulder and went back into the town and to the villainous priest's house again. When he got there the old scoundrel was just about to lock his door. And the butcher, coming up with the sheep on his back, called out: "Good sir, may God keep you who watches over us all!" The priest returned his greeting and asked him where he came from.

"From Abbeville," said the butcher. "I've been to the market at Oisemont, where all I bought was this sheep. He's a good one with a nice fat rump. I tell you what—I'm not a stingy fellow—if you'll give me a lodging for the night, seeing how comfortably fixed you are, we'll dine off this sheep. For I've had a hard job carrying it as far as this."

The priest, who was always greedy for other men's goods and who liked a dead sheep better than four live men, thought the other was speaking the truth, and he said: "Yes, certainly, I'll be glad to. Even if there were three of you, I would be more than happy to give you shelter. No man has found me slow to extend this kind of courtesy or to do honor to a stranger. You seem to be a very good sort of man. Tell me, what is your name?"

"Sir," said the butcher, "so help me God, my name is David, and it was given to me at the font, with all the necessary oils and unguents. But I am weary with tramping the roads. May God never look on the man to whom this heavy beast belonged! I've carried him far enough; it's time now for me to set him down before a good fire."

With that they went into the house, where a good fire was burning. The butcher put down his beast and, looking about, asked for a hatchet, which was quickly brought to him. Then he killed the sheep and skinned it, threw the pelt down on a bench, and hung up the carcass in plain sight.

"By God, sir!" the butcher said. "Come here and look at this sheep, for the love of God! See how nice and fat he is! He was a heavy burden all right, and I carried him a long way. Well now, help yourself to him. Make a roast of his shoulders. Put a full pot on to boil for the servants. Without exaggeration, I've never seen such good meat. Let it cook over the fire. See how tender and succulent it is. It will be done even before the sauce is prepared." "Good guest," said the priest, "do as you wish, I won't get in your way." "Have them lay the table then," said the butcher. "It is ready! All we have to do now is wash our hands and light the candles!"

Well, my lords, I won't tell you any lie, but the priest had a mistress of whom he was so jealous that when he had company of an evening he made her stay in her room. But that night he brought her down to join his guest at this joyous dinner.

They all ate well, served richly with good meat and good wine. And afterward, the priest had a bed made up for the butcher, with white linen sheets on it, all very comfortable. The priest called his maidservant and said: "My dear, see that our guest is comfortable and that nothing displeases him." Then he and his lady went off to bed.

The butcher remained by the fire. Never in all his life had he been so wonderfully well received and lodged, never had he been so comfortable. He called the maidservant to him and said: "Sweet sister, come here and let us talk a bit. For if you will take me for a lover, on my word I promise you you won't lose by it."

"Oh, sir guest," she said, "what a thing to say! I know nothing of such things!"

"By God," he said, "you'll do it all right when you hear my proposition."

"Well, tell it to me and I'll see."

"All right then," he said. "If you will do as I say and fulfill all my desires, I swear to God, on whom I call with a true heart, that you shall have the skin of my sheep."

"Dear guest, don't say such things! You would make a poor hermit! To ask such a thing of me! And think what evil might come of it!"

"Dear God," he said, "how plump you are! What a lovely behind!"

"But I daren't! Tomorrow you will tell my mistress on me."

"Sister mine, as my soul belongs to God, I swear never to tell her or to accuse you of anything as long as I live."

So at last she let him have his will of her and stayed with him all night until the day broke. Then she got up, lit the fire, did her chores, and went to milk the cows. And early that morning the priest also awoke and went with his clerk to the church to say mass and perform his duties. But the priest's mistress remained in bed.

The butcher got up too and put on his clothes and shoes without delay, for it was getting late, and went straight into the bedroom to say goodbye to his hostess. He pulled at the door catch and opened the door; the lady awoke, opened her eyes, and saw her guest standing there before her. She asked him how he'd got there and if he had forgotten something. "Lady," he said, "I come to thank you. You have given me good lodging and treated me wonderfully well." And, as he spoke, the butcher drew near to her bedside, laid his hand on the pillow, and drew back the sheet. Then he saw her beautiful white throat and her bosom and her fair breasts. "O God," he cried, "I see miracles! Saint Mary and Saint Romacles! How lucky this priest is to have such a lady to lie naked by his side! As I honor the saints, she is fit for a king! If I had the time, how I would like to lie a little with her! I would rise new-made and cured of all my ills."

"Dear guest," said the lady, "by Saint Germain, you don't ask for very much! Begone! Take away your hand! My lord will soon finish his office. He will be only too ready to think himself betrayed if he finds you in his chamber. He will never love me again. You will have compromised me and brought me to ruin."

"Lady," said the butcher to comfort her, "never will I budge from here, not for any man alive, not even if the priest came in; for if he should say a single foolish or insulting word, I would kill him on the spot. Now then, grant me my wish and do as I say, and I will give you my sheepskin thick with wool and a good sum of money besides."

"Sir, I will do nothing of the kind. For I can see you are so vain that tomorrow you would tell everybody about it."

"Lady," said he, "by my faith, as long as I live I will not tell a soul, neither man nor woman, not for all the saints in Rome."

And he spoke so well and promised so much that at last the lady softened and granted him all he desired. The butcher found joyful refreshment. And, when he had taken his pleasure, he left at once—he had no reason to stay longer—and went to the church. There the priest was beginning a prayer with one of his clerks, and just as he got to the *Jube domine,* in came the butcher.

"Sir," said the butcher, "many thanks for the fine lodging you have given me and for your fine treatment. But there is one thing I would like to ask of you, and I pray you to grant it to me. Be so good as to buy my sheepskin. You will be sparing me a great deal of trouble. It's a good skin, by God, with three good pounds of wool on it. It's worth three sous, but you can have it for two, and I'll take it as a favor that you buy it."

"Dear guest," said the priest, "out of love for you I will buy it willingly, for you are a good companion and a good man altogether. Come back and see me as often as you like."

And thereupon the butcher sold him the sheepskin, made his adieus, and went away.

Meanwhile the lady had arisen. She was indeed a pretty creature and daintily dressed in a green tunic that was beautifully folded in running pleats, which out of vanity she had arranged under her belt. Her eyes were bright and full of laughter, and altogether she was very beautiful and pleasing to behold. When she sat down at the table, she saw the maidservant, who was about to take away the sheepskin. The lady stopped her and said: "Hey there! What do you think you are doing with that skin?"

"Lady," said the girl, "that's my business. I want to hang it in the sun to cure the leather."

"Oh no!" said the mistress. "Leave it right where it is and go about your work. It's not in the way."

"Lady, I have done all my work. I get up earlier than you do. And by my faith, no matter what ails you, you should speak civilly."

"Go away," said the lady, "and let the skin be! Don't you dare lay a hand on it or interfere with it at all."

"Oh no, by God, lady! I will do whatever I want with it, for it belongs to me."

"What! Do you say it is yours?"

"Yes, I do indeed!"

"Put down that skin! You can go hang or go shit, as you please! Oh, how you upset me when you put on those airs! You slut, you lousy whore! Get out! Leave my house at once!"

"Lady, you must be mad to insult me for wanting my own property. And even if you swore by all the saints that it was yours, it would still belong to me."

"Just the same, get out of this house! Go drown yourself! I have no use for your services. You're a wanton and a fool. Even if my lord had sworn to keep you, I still wouldn't have you here. How I hate you now!"

"May whoever serves you for a single day be cursed," said the servant. "I shall wait until my master comes and then I'll go. But first I'll complain to him about you."

"Complain then, you little fool, you whore, you stinker, you bawd, you bastard!"

"Bastard? That word was not well chosen, lady. I suppose the brats you had with the priest are legitimate!"

"By God's passion, put down the skin or you will pay dearly for it! By all the saints in heaven, you'd be better off to Arras or as far away as Cologne!"

And with that the mistress seized her distaff and gave the girl such a blow that she cried out: "By the virtue of Saint Mary! You have beaten me for no reason. You'll have bought that sheepskin dear if I should die of this beating." Then she began to weep and to complain so loudly that the noise brought the priest into the house.

"What is it?" he said. "Who has done this to you?"

"My mistress, master, and for no fault of mine."

"No fault? But you must have done something to make her treat you so badly."

"Before God, sir, it was because of that skin that hangs there by the fire. Last night when you went to bed you ordered me to take care of our guest David and to see that he was comfortable. I did as you ordered, and he gave me the sheepskin. Truly he did! And I swear by all the saints that I well deserved it."

Hearing what she said, the priest understood that his guest had tricked him and sold him a skin which he had already given away. He was full of rage, but he didn't dare speak his mind. So he turned to his mistress and said: "Lady, may God save me, this was a wicked thing to do. You cannot care much for me if you beat my servants."

"Bah!" said his mistress. "She wants to take my sheepskin. If you but knew the shameful things she said to me! Would you take her side who shamed me for mothering your children? You do ill to let her insult me and befoul everything with her evil tongue. I don't know what will come of it, but I will never let her have my skin. I say that it is not hers!"

"Then whose is it?" said the priest.

"Why, mine!" replied his mistress.

"Yours?" said the priest. "By what right is it yours?"

"By Saint Aceus!" said she. "Our guest slept in our house, on my bed and in my sheets, if you must know everything."

"My dear," said the priest, "by the faith you promised when first you came to live with me, now tell me: is that sheepskin really yours?"

"By the holy Our Father," she said, "it is!"

And the little servant: "Good master, don't believe her! He gave the skin to me."

"Hah!" said the mistress. "You baseborn whore! All he gave you was the runs. Go on, get out of my house, and a curse go with you!"

"By the holy image of Compiègne," said the priest, "lady, you are wrong to talk like that."

"No, I'm not," she said, "for I hate her to death, she is such a liar, the dirty little thief."

"Lady, what have I ever stolen from you?"

"You slut—my barley and my wheat and my peas and my bacon and my best bread. Really, my lord, you were very spineless to stand for her so long in this house. Now pay her her wages and, by God, get rid of her."

"Now, lady, understand me, please," said the priest, "what I want to know is which of you two should have this skin. Now tell me, who gave it to you?"

"Our guest, when he went away."

"By the ribs of Saint Martin!" said the priest. "The truth is that he left early this morning, before the sun had risen. My God, how faithless you are to swear so boldly!"

"On the contrary, my lord. He said goodbye very politely before he left."

"Was he then at your rising?" asked the priest.

"Oh no, he wasn't! I was still lying down. I took no notice of him when I saw him standing there before me. But I must explain to you that . . ."

"What!" said the priest. "What did he say to you when he took his leave?"

"My lord, you are too suspicious. He said: 'I commend you to Jesus,' and thereupon he left. He never said another word to me, nor did he ask anything of me that might be to your dishonor. But you, you go sniffing after some treachery. You never have trusted me—as if you had no proof that I was a virtuous woman, as, thank God, I am. You're always looking for deceit, and you've locked me up here as in a prison—my face has gone all pale from lack of sun. I never stir from your house, but stay here like a bird in a cage. You want too much for the meat and drink you give me."

"Ah!" cried the priest, "you crazy bitch, you've had it too good here! Another word and I'll beat you half to death! Now I'm sure that he slept with you. Tell me, why didn't you cry out? You ought to have stopped the affair. Go on, get out of my house! As for me, I'll go to the altar this minute and swear never to lie in your bed again." And, too weak with rage to stand, he fell into a chair and sat there, brooding, sad, and full of rage.

When his mistress saw how angry he was, she was terribly sorry she had picked a quarrel with him and moved him to rage; and, afraid that he might hurt her, she ran to her room.

No sooner had she gone than the shepherd came running in, for he had counted his sheep and one of them was missing. He did not know what had become of it. He burst into the house, rubbing his sides. The priest, who was reading in his breviary, still all hot and furious, looked up and said: "What's wrong now, damn you, you old rascal? Where are you coming from? What's going on, you whoreson stupid clod? You should be out watching the sheep. In two seconds I'll give you a good beating."

"Sir, I've lost one of our sheep, the best one in the flock. I don't know who could have stolen it."

"So now you've lost a sheep, have you? You should be hanged for watching them so badly!"

"Sir," said the shepherd, "please listen to me. Last night as I was returning to town, I met a stranger, a man I had never seen before, neither in the fields nor in town nor on the road. He was eying the animals, and he questioned me at length about their owner; and I told him it was our lord the priest. It is my belief that it was he who stole the sheep."

"By all the saints in heaven!" cried the priest. "It was David, our guest who slept here in the house. Oh, he has played me some fine tricks! To lay my whole household and then to sell me my own sheepskin! How stupid I was not to have been more careful! You can learn something every day! How true are the sayings of the wise men: 'He wiped my nose with my own handkerchief; with my own dough he baked me a tart.' Would you recognize the skin of the animal?"

"Yes, sir," said the shepherd, "by my faith, I would recognize it easily if I saw it. He has been in my flock for seven years." He took the skin and examined well the head and the ears and saw that it was the skin of his sheep. "Oh, alas!" he cried then. "By God, sir, it is Corniaus, the beast I loved best! By Saint Vincent, there was never a better or more peaceable animal in the whole flock. There wasn't such a nice fat one in a hundred."

"Come here, my lady," the priest cried then, "and you, my girl, come forward. Now, on your honor, answer my questions. What is your claim in this skin?"

"Sir," said the servant, "I claim it all."

"And you, my lady, what do you say to that?"

"My lord," said the priest's mistress, "as my soul belongs to God, the skin is mine by right."

"And I say that neither of you shall have it. I bought it with my own money and I shall keep it. The butcher came to the church while I was reading the psalter and offered it to me. By Saint Peter, the true apostle, neither she nor you shall have it unless it be granted you by an impartial judgment."

And now, my lords, you who understand these matters, Eustace of Amiens prays you, by the love he bears you, that you decide in this case and that you judge wisely and fairly. Let each of you give his opinion.

[43]

Who most deserves the skin of this beast,
The little servant, the priestess, or priest?

"Le Boucher d'Abbeville," preserved in four manuscripts of the thirteenth and fourteenth centuries, was one of the most popular fabliaux. The author, Eustache d'Amiens, is known to posterity only through the mention he makes of himself in the epilogue of this work. Despite his obscurity, we may surmise from the impeccable composition of "The Butcher" that Eustache was a professional writer of some importance, surely the equal of his more illustrious compatriots from Picardy, Adam de la Halle and Jean Bodel.

No ancient source or analogue for this tale is known to exist, but the poet did draw on tried and effective elements of the comic plot. The tale belongs to the large group of stories of similar theme designated by folklorists as *the lover's gift regained*. It has been compared with the eighth tale of the first day of the *Decameron*, which was adapted by La Fontaine as "A Femme Avare Galant Escroc" ("For a Stingy Woman, a Swindling Lover") and with Chaucer's "Shipman's Tale," although these works bear only a remote resemblance to the fabliau.

The popularity of Eustache's tale brought about an almost immediate imitation by one of his contemporaries, Milon d'Amiens, whose "Le Prestre et le Chevalier" ("The Priest and the Knight"; c. 1300) exploited essentially the same situation, substituting a knight for a butcher. Milon, however, turned the lively style and inspiration of "The Butcher" into a flat and rather uninteresting narrative. Apparently no further imitations of this fabliau were produced in France, but it had a certain popularity in Germany, where it was turned into prose in the eighteenth century by Meissner and subsequently back into verse by Langbein.

Edition: John Orr, *Eustache d'Amiens: Le Boucher d'Abbeville* (London, 1947).

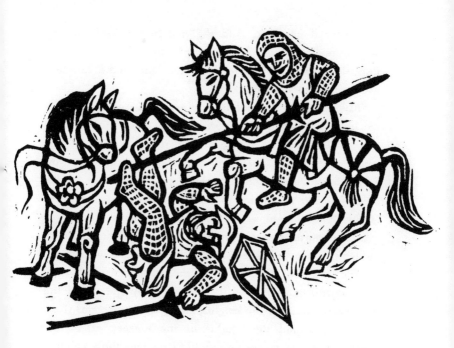

THE KNIGHT WHO REGAINED
HIS LADY'S LOVE

Without further delay, I shall tell a story about a knight and a lady which came to pass, so it is written, in Normandy not long ago. This knight wished to make the lady his mistress, and, so that she might be certain he loved her, took great pains to accomplish all the deeds which he knew would please her. I don't want to make a long story of it, but this knight pleaded with her so long that one day the lady addressed him and asked him what reason he could give for demanding her love, since not one day in all his life had he accomplished knightly deeds in her honor or done those things which might have pleased her and by which he might have earned her love. And she told him, laughingly and without malice, that he would never be the master of her love until she knew how he bore shield and lance and if he could use them to good effect.

"My lady," said the knight, "do not be distressed, but give me leave to enter a tournament against your husband and you be at his gate in such a place that you may see all the action of the joust. Then, if it suits you, you will know how I bear lance and shield." The lady did not hesitate to give the knight her permission to engage in the tournament; and forthwith the knight went off to enter his name in the lists.

So the tournament was arranged, and worthy knights were bidden to come and take part in it, word being sent throughout the land until the very day of the tournament; for everyone was full of ardor and impatience. They announced the day and the hour to the knights, and great numbers of them appeared. Behold the knights of the tourney assembled, great, proud, and fierce. You should have seen those knights, when it came time to joust, putting on their hauberks and lacing their helmets! Each of them was soon ready.

The two knights who had called the tournament were in the lists first, armed and riding swift horses, and both of them ready to shatter lances. Without delay they rushed together; their shields in place and their lances couched, they slackened reins and charged, bracing themselves nobly in the stirrups. They broke and splintered their lances. Then, neither sparing himself, they went at it with their swords, each as best he knew how. The knight who had called the tournament and sworn on his soul to joust against the lady's huband charged at once, recklessly and more swiftly than a well-aimed arrow leaves the bow. He brought the husband down with his leveled lance, nor could the breast strap or girths keep him up, but saddle, horse, and man came down all together. When the lady saw this, she was sad, on the one hand, for the misfortune that had befallen her husband, but happy, on the other hand, that her lover had fought so well.

Why should I spin out my tale? The knights had all begun to tourney well, when to their grief a sin invaded the tournament, for one of the knights was killed, I don't know how or why, and everyone grew sad and gloomy. They buried him under an elm, and afterward, because it was late, they gave up tourneying. Then each of them went to his lodging; and the lady, delaying no longer, sent two boys to inform the knight that, if he wanted her to love him and to take him as her lover forever, he might come to speak to her that night. The knight, who was overjoyed at these words, said he would come very willingly. "Even if I were cut to pieces," he said, "I would not fail to come." And so the boys left him.

When night came he could hardly wait to go there where he was expected. A maiden kept constant watch for his coming, and when he arrived he greeted her. In great fear and apprehension she led him into a room and told him to wait there until her lady came to him. Then the maiden left and going to her mistress told her the news: the knight had come and was waiting in that room. "Are you telling me the truth?" said she. "Yes, on my soul." "Then I shall go," said the lady, "as soon as my husband has gone to bed." The knight, meanwhile, because the lady was so long in coming, grew very bored and could not keep from lying down and falling asleep; he was so weary from having borne arms all day. The lady, sorry to be so late, went to him as soon as she could. When she saw that he was very apparently asleep, she did not nudge or shake him, but turned at once and went away.

She called her chambermaid and said: "Go quickly, without lingering, and tell that knight from me he is to leave at once." The maid asked her why, and she said: "I'll give you the reason all right: because he is asleep." "By God's soul," said the servant, "it seems to me you are in the wrong." "You're lying, wench!" said the lady. "He ought to have remained awake all night long for a single kiss from such a lady as I am. That is why I am so grieved: for I know that if he had indeed loved me he would not have acted like that for a hundred pounds. Go, send him on his way."

The servant went to the knight, who was asleep leaning on his elbow, and gave him a push. Immediately he leapt to his feet and cried: "Ah, at last, my lady, you are welcome, but you have been a long time coming." "You have greeted me for nothing, sir knight," said the maiden. "Very soon you will hear a different kind of news. My lady has sent me, she who lies abed by her husband's side, to tell you never to be so bold or so reckless as to approach her in whatever place she may be." "What! Tell me why, young miss!" "That I will: because you ought not to have fallen asleep when you were waiting for such a noble lady, so beautiful, so white, so tender, and so valiant as my lady is." "Damsel," he said, "on my soul, I have done wrong, it is true; but I beg you, for charity's sake, that I may have your permission to go there where my lady and her husband lie abed. For you must know that I have never wanted anything more." "By my faith," said the maiden, "I will grant you that willingly."

The knight, delighted to hear this, ran to his lady's chamber—there was nothing wrong with his legs. As was the custom, a lamp was burning in the room. The knight went his way and came straight to the bed, where he stood at a little distance with his naked sword in his hand. The husband, awakened by the gleaming of the sword, opened his eyes and saw him there. The knight did not budge. "Who are you?" said the husband. The knight, who saw no reason to dally, spoke and said: "I am the knight who was killed this morning. Surely you must remember. I am indeed he." "And what brings you here?" "My lord, I am in great affliction, and never will my soul leave this place unless that lady who lies with you will pardon me for a single wrong I did her when I was alive. May the God of heaven grant you honor and joy and many of his gifts! Beseech her to forgive me. For I have told you the reason and the occasion of my coming here."

"Lady, my lady," said the husband, "if you bear a grudge against this knight, or if you are angry with him, I beg you to pardon him for his misdeed, for God's sake and for the good of his soul." "I shall do nothing of the kind," said the lady. "You're troubling your head for nothing; it's only a false apparition or some such beast which is plaguing us all night." "Really," said her husband, "I don't believe it is." "No," said the knight, "I am no such thing, my lord; I believe in God and in his mother." "By the faith you owe Saint Peter," said the husband, "whence comes this anger and this wrath which the lady feels toward you?" "My lord," said the knight, "in no way may I reveal it, for if I suffer now, I shall fare worse if I utter a word of it." "Indeed you shall be pardoned, sir knight," said the lady. "I don't want to distress you further." "Thank you, my sweet friend," said he, "for I ask no more of you." Then he went away at once. His undertaking had turned out well. But if he had not acted thus, he would never have recovered the love which lately had been granted him.

Pierres d'Anfol, who first invented and wrote this fabliau, did it only to teach those who hear it and speak about it. For no one has heard it who has not been the better for it, unless he was too possessed by wickedness.

"Le Chevalier Qui Recovra l'Amor de Sa Dame," like "William and the Falcon," is closer in tone to the courtly tale than to the general run of fabliaux. But the stratagem whereby, as in "William and the Falcon," the husband is made a party to his own cuckolding is very much in the tradition of the fabliau. Moreover, as in many fabliaux, there is an element of satire on the courtly romances: a lover falling asleep when he is about to attain his greatest desire must have evoked a wry smile from an audience adept in the traditions of the court of love.

Yet it is this very episode of the sleeping lover which connects the tale to a very ancient narrative tradition. Similar situations are found in Arabic tales and in folk stories of Jutland, Ireland, and India; it is also a frequent episode in the romances of the Grail. The source of this fabliau is not known, and apparently it was not often retold. There is, to be sure, the early thirteenth-century *Versnovelle* (*Tales in Verse*) of Moriz von Craun, which may well derive from a common ancestor; and the fabliau was reworked at least once by Barthélemy Imbert in the eighteenth century from the prose adaptation (1779–1781) of Legrand d'Aussy.

The Pierres d'Anfol whose name appears at the end of the work is certainly not the author of the fabliau. The name can only be a French form of Petrus Alphonsi, the name of a converted Spanish Jew who was born in 1062 and who compiled a collection of didactic tales, mostly from Arab sources, entitled *Disciplina Clericalis* (*Instruction for the Clergy;* early twelfth century). Since this fabliau is found neither in Petrus' collection nor in the Old French adaptation of it, it is safe to conclude that the actual author sought to gain authority for his composition by attributing it to a famous author, a procedure not uncommon in the Middle Ages.

Edition: Johnston-Owen, pp. 78–84.

THE MILLER AND
THE TWO CLERICS

There were once two poor fellows of the minor clergy who were born in the same region and in the same city. They were friends and deacons of a woodland church, where they found a living, until, as happens often and again, they fell on hard times, which is a great pity for poor people. They were heavy at heart when they considered their state of affairs, nor did they see any way out of it. For they did not know how to earn their living, either in their own country or anywhere else, and they were ashamed to beg their bread out of regard for their order, as well as for other reasons. They had no possessions by which they might keep themselves alive, and they didn't know where to turn.

One Sunday they met outside the church, and they went for a walk about the town in order to talk things over. "Listen to me," one of them said to the other, "we are helpless because we cannot earn our livings; and now hunger, which vanquishes everything, has got hold of us. Nobody can defend us against it, and we have nothing to draw upon. Have you put by anything at all by which we might keep ourselves going?" The other one answered: "By Saint Denis, I can't think of anything except that I have a friend to whom I suggest we go and ask for a bushel of wheat at the current price; he will very willingly give me credit, and at long term, until Saint John's Day, to tide us over this bad year." Then the first one said: "That's a piece of luck for us; for I have a brother who owns a fat mare. I'll go get her while you get the wheat, and we'll become bakers. There is no load too shameful to bear if it will get us through this bad year." And they did this without further delay.

Then they brought their wheat to the mill, which was at a great distance, more than two leagues away. It was a mill with a millrace near a little wood. There was no town or farm or any house nearby except the house of the miller, who knew his trade only too well. The clerics undid the gate at once and threw their sacks inside. Then they put their mare in a meadow by the millrace. One of them remained outside to keep an eye on things, and the other went in to get the miller started at their work. But the miller had gone into hiding. He had indeed seen the clerics coming, and I think he wanted a part of their wheat.

When the cleric came running into the miller's house, he found his wife at her spinning. "Lady," he said, "by Saint Martin, where is the owner of the mill? He ought to come and help us." "Sir cleric," said she, "it's no trouble at all. You will find him in that wood right near the mill, if you will be so kind as to go there." And the cleric set out quickly to find him. His friend, who was waiting for him, grew impatient that he stayed so long and came running into the house. "Lady," he said, "for the love of God, where has my companion gone?" "Sir," said she, "on my honor, he went in search of my husband who has just left the house." So she sent one cleric after the other, while the miller came around quickly to the mill. With his wife's help he took both sacks and mare and hid them in his barn. Then he returned to the mill.

The two clerics looked everywhere, and finally they also returned to the mill. "Miller," they said, "God be with you! For the love of God, help us out." "My lords," said he, "how may I do so?" "In faith, with the wheat we have here." But, when they went to get the wheat, they found neither sacks nor mare. They looked at one another. "What's this?" said one. "We are robbed!" "Yes," said the other, "so it seems to me. For our sins we are undone!" Then both cried out: "Alas! Alas! Help us, Saint Nicholas!" "What's wrong with you?" said the miller. "Why do you cry so loud?" "Miller, we have surely lost everything. A misfortune has befallen us, for we have neither mare nor anything. And that was our whole fortune." "Lords," said the miller, "I know nothing about this." "Sir," they said, "there's nothing you can do except to tell us where we may go to look for what we have lost." "Lords," he said, "I can't help you very much, but go look in that wood there near the mill." The two clerics set out and at once went into the woods; and the miller went his way.

They looked high and low until the sun had set; and then one of the clerics said to the other: "Surely it is truly said that he's a fool who puts himself out for nothing. Wealth comes and goes like straws blown by the wind. Let's go find a lodging for the night." "And where shall we go?" "To the miller's, in whose mill we were. May God grant us lodging in Saint Martin's name!"

They went straight to the miller's house; but he was not pleased at their coming. At once he asked them: "What has Saint Nicholas done for you?" "Miller," they said, "not one thing or another." "Then," said he, "you'd better earn other goods. For what you've lost is a long way off; you won't have it for present needs." "Miller," they said, "that may well be. But put us up for Saint Sylvester's sake. We don't know where else to go at this hour." The miller took thought and decided that he would be worse than a dog if he didn't provide something for them out of their own belongings, as he was well able. "My lords," he said, "I have nothing but the floor to offer you; that you shall have and nothing more." "Miller," they said, "that is enough."

The peasant did not have many in his household. With himself there were only four: his daughter, who deserves to be mentioned first, his wife, and a little baby. The daughter was beautiful and charming, and to protect her against her own warmth, the miller put her in a cupboard every night, and there she slept. The miller would lock her in and pass her the key through an opening, and then he would go to bed.

But let us return to our clerics. In the evening at supper-time, the miller brought bread and milk and eggs and cheese, country fare, and he gave each of the clerics a good share. One of them supped with the maiden and the other with the miller and his wife. In the hearth was a little andiron with a ring on it that could be taken off and put back again. The cleric who ate with the maiden took the ring from the andiron and hid it well. That night, when they went to bed, the cleric watched the daughter carefully and saw how the miller locked her in the cupboard and threw her the key.

When they had settled down for the night, the cleric nudged his companion and said: "Friend, I want to go and speak to the miller's daughter, who is locked up in the cupboard." "Do you want to start a quarrel," said the other, "and stir up a tempest in the house? Truth is you are a rogue. Evil can soon come of this." "Even if I die," said the first, "I must go and see if I can make anything of her." He quickly jumped out of bed and went straight to the cupboard. He drew near it and scratched on it a little, and she heard him. "Who is it out there?" she said. "It is he who for your sake is so grieved and so unhappy that, unless you have pity on him, he will never feel joy again. It is he with whom you supped and who brings you a gold ring—you never had such a treasure. It is known and proved that its stone has such power that any woman, no matter how light she may be or how she may wanton about, will remain a virgin if she has it on her finger in the morning. Here, I make you a gift of it." At once she held out the key to him; and he quickly unlocked the chest. He got in and she squeezed over. And so they could take their pleasure, for there was no one to disturb them.

Before daybreak the miller's wife got up from beside her husband and all naked went into the courtyard. And she passed before the cleric where he lay abed. When he saw her go by, he thought of his friend who was taking his pleasure in the cupboard, and he had a great longing for the same kind of pleasure. He thought he would trick the wife on her way back. But then he thought he would not, for fear of what mad consequences might ensue. And then again he thought of a new stratagem. He jumped out of bed and went straight to the bed where the miller lay. He carried away the child in its cradle; and when the wife came in the door, the cleric pinched the baby's ear, whereupon it awoke and cried out. The wife, who had been going to her own bed, when she heard the cry turned about and went in that direction. When she found the cradle she was reassured, and she lifted the cover and lay down beside the cleric, who hugged her tight. He drew her to him and squeezed her so tight in his pleasure that he quite crushed her. In amazement she allowed him to do what he liked.

Meanwhile, the other cleric, when he heard the cock crow, felt he had been lingering too long. He made himself ready, took his leave of the maiden, and slipped out of the chest. He went straight to his own bed where his companion lay, but when he found the cradle he was dismayed, and no wonder. He was frightened, but nonetheless he felt a little further; and when he came on two heads he knew he must be wrong. So he went quickly to the bed where the miller was lying and lay down beside him. The miller had not yet awakened and noticed nothing. "Comrade," said the cleric, "what are you doing? He who never has anything to say is worth nothing. On my word, I've had a fine night, God save me! She's a warm little girl, the miller's daughter. That kind of pleasure is very wicked indeed, but there is great pleasure in the cupboard. Go, my friend, slip in now yourself and get your share of the bacon. There's plenty left before you get to the rind. I've bent her back seven times tonight, but she still hasn't got her fill. All she got in return was the ring from the andiron. I've done a good job."

When the miller heard this trick, he seized the cleric by the collar; and the cleric, when he saw what was up, grabbed the miller and treated him so roughly that he almost strangled him. The wife began to kick the other cleric who was lying beside her. "Husband," she said, "what's going on? Please, let's get up at once. Those clerics are strangling each other over there." "Never you mind," said the cleric, "let them be, let the fools kill each other." (He knew very well that his companion was the stronger of the two.)

When the miller managed to break loose, he ran at once to light the fire. And when he saw his wife lying with the cleric, he shouted: "Get up, you brazen whore. How did you get in there? Now it's all up with you." "Husband," she said, "it's not quite as you say. For if I am a brazen whore, I was tricked into it. But you're a bold-faced thief, for you have made away with these clerics' sacks of wheat and their mare, for which you will be hanged. It's all stuck away in your barn."

The two clerics took hold of the miller and came little short of milling him like wheat, so hard did they beat and bruise him. They kicked and cuffed him until he gave them back all their wheat. Then they went to another mill to get their wheat ground. They got Saint Martin's lodging, and they worked so well at their new trade that they got through the bad year and gave thanks up and down to God and to Saint Nicholas.

The anonymous fabliau of "Le Meunier et les Deux Clers" is one of the most humorous, successful, and classically conceived tales of the genre to survive, a fact which explains perhaps why it captivated the three greatest storytellers of all time: Boccaccio (the sixth tale of the ninth day of the *Decameron*), Chaucer ("The Reeve's Tale"), and La Fontaine ("Le Berceau," "The Cradle"). It belongs to a group of tales designated by folklorists as *the cradle,* and is found in such widely different versions as that related by Rüdiger von Müner as "Irregang und Girregar" from Von der Hagen's *Gesammtabenteuer* (*Collected Tales,* Tale LV). There is even a late medieval Latin adaptation, "De Duobus Studentibus Qui Hospitem cum Uxore et Filia Inebriarunt" ("Two Students Intoxicated by a Wife and Her Daughter"). A second fabliau, "Gombert et les Deux Clers" ("Gombert and the Two Clerics"), by Jean Bodel, shows a close affinity in its central intrigue, but the fabliau translated here is far more interesting because the author has developed the characters further and has plausibly motivated the actions of the two clerics, and it was this version of the fabliau which provided the model for Chaucer's adaptation.

Edition: W. F. Bryan and Germaine Dempster, *Sources and Analogues of Chaucer's Canterbury Tales* (New York, 1958), pp. 126–146.

BERANGER
LONGBOTTOM

by Garin

I have made and recited many tales and fabliaux, both old and new. I have been at it for more than two years, and, by Saint John, I don't think I shall compose any more, except for this one of Beranger Longbottom. Haven't you heard it yet? I swear, I'll tell it to you now; I won't delay another moment. Listen to what Garin has to tell!

There once lived in Lombardy, a country whose people are not very brave, a certain knight, who took to wife a lady of gentle birth, the daughter of a rich lord. The knight himself was the son of a peasant, a moneylender who was rich and prosperous and had plenty of wine and wheat, sheep and cows, and bushels and pecks of hard coin. The lord owed the usurer more money than he could pay, and so he gave his daughter to the usurer's son. So are noble families debased, and so do lords and counts all fall from their noble state, contracting low marriages for the sake of money. They do themselves a great wrong and should indeed be ashamed. Of people like this, who love money more than knighthood, bad knights are born, base and cowardly. So does nobility perish.

But to tell the story as I have heard it, the lord wasted no time, but fitted his daughter out and married her to this peasant. With his own hands he made him a knight, so I have heard, and this new knight led her away.

They lived together for more than ten years. And this knight loved to lie about; he wouldn't have given two cloves of garlic for all the praise and glory of knighthood. He loved tarts and hot custards and truly despised common folk. When his wife became aware of what an ignoble fellow her husband was and that there wasn't a worse knight when it came to taking up and bearing arms (he would rather have pitched hay than have handled a shield or a lance), then she knew, without doubt, because he was such a great talker, that he was not descended of knights nor was he of gentle birth. Therefore she reminded him of her own lineage which boasted so many valiant knights. "They were brave and proud in bearing arms," she said, "they did not like to stay at home."

The peasant knight understood well that she said this only for him. "Lady," he replied, "I have a great name. You do not have a brave knight in your family but I can find a braver one in mine, more valiant and of greater prowess. I am no lazy knight, but the best knight of all, I swear! Lady, that you will see tomorrow, if I can but find my enemies. To-morrow, at all costs, I am determined to do so, for they have basely challenged me. Indeed, not one of them shall get away alive. I will bring them to such grief that I will cut off all their heads. They shall all die, come what may."

And so they left the matter that night. And in the morning, at break of day, the knight rose early and called for his arms. He had them arm his body richly, for he had a very fine set of arms, all new and shiny. When the knight was armed and mounted on his horse, he tried to think what he should do and how he could deceive his wife so that she might think him a worthy knight. He spurred his horse toward a great thick wood near his house, and he rode straight into that forest without stopping. When he had got well into the woods, he stopped beneath a tree and tied his horse. His shield he hung on an oak there.

And now listen to what the fool did! He drew his sword, which was bright and well polished, and with it, so it seems to me, he dealt his shield more than a hundred blows, so that he knocked it all to splinters, cut it all up and ruined it. Then he took his lance and broke it into four pieces. After that he got into the saddle and posted down a valley straight to his house. He had but a splinter of his lance and only a quarter of his shield, which he had borne away whole that morning.

He rode up with the reins in his hand, and his wife came out to meet him and held the stirrup for him to dismount. This knight, in the grandest manner, proudly kicked her away with his foot and said: "Stand back at once! For know this: it is not right that you should touch such a worthy and celebrated knight as I am. There is not one knight in all your family who is so gallant and so bold. I am in no way vanquished or defeated; rather, I have earned the glory of knighthood." The lady was all astonished when she saw the shield hacked to pieces and the wood of the lance broken. In the face of such evidence, she did not know what to say or do. She was afraid that he might beat her, for he threatened her and warned her off from coming near him or touching him. She kept her mouth shut and said not a word in reply.

Well, what shall I tell you? The knight made use of this ruse to hold his wife in low esteem and to despise all her family, which she did not take at all kindly.

One day the knight once again returned from the woods with his shield again pierced and hacked to bits; but he was not wounded or hurt, nor was his helmet scratched. He was hale and whole from top to toe and neither weary nor beaten. And this time the lady did not believe him when he said that he had put to death so many warriors and confounded his enemies and taken them in battle and hanged them. The lady saw well that he was a coward by nature and that he had deceived her with a trick. She promised herself that if he went to the wood again she would go after him and find out what knights he fought with and how he bore himself.

So the lady made her plans, and in the morning, when the knight had armed himself and said that he was off to kill three knights who menaced him and sought to do him great harm (he complained that they were looking for their chance), the lady suggested that he take three or four of his servants with him, so that he might do battle in greater safety. To which the knight replied: "Lady, I will not take one with me. All alone I shall give them so much trouble that not one of them shall escape with his life." Then he went on his way and in great anger struck out for the woods.

The lady found some arms, armed herself like a knight, and mounted a horse. She did not delay, but set out after her husband, who was already deep in the woods. Already he had hung his shield on the oak and was striking at it with his sword and cutting it to pieces. He made such noise and such destruction that anyone who had heard it would have thought that there were a hundred or a thousand devils there. Don't think I am lying! He really made a great clamor and brouhaha.

The lady stopped for a moment, and when she saw what was going on she was astonished and bewildered. But, when she had listened enough, she spurred her horse at her husband and cried out: "Sir knight! Sir knight! What madness is this that you cut up my woods? I am a sorry knight if I let you escape without hacking you limb from limb. Why are you mistreating your shield, which has done you no wrong? You have engaged in a foolish business here today. Cursed be he who holds you in esteem, since you have made war on your own shield!"

When the base knight heard these words, he was astounded and dismayed. He did not recognize the lady. The naked sword fell from his hands, and the blood left his veins. "My lord," he said, "have mercy, for God's sake! If I have done you any wrong, I will make it up to you without any trouble. Very willingly I will give you goods and money, as much as you want."

"So may God save me," said the lady, "you will sing another tune before you leave this place. For I will offer you a choice: either you must joust with me—and if you fall, I will have no mercy on you, but you shall lose your head at once, or else I shall get down on foot and bend over, and you shall kiss my arse, right in the middle, if you please. I order you to choose which you prefer."

This peasant knight, who was very much afraid and full of

cowardice, said that he had no wish to joust. "My lord," he said, "I have taken a vow not to joust with any man alive. But get down, if it's no trouble, and I will do whatever suits you." The lady did not care to delay. She dismounted, lifted up her tunic, and bent over before him. "My lord," she said, "put your face here!"

The knight looked into the crevice, and because the hole and the other parts seemed to run together, he thought that he had never seen such a long arsehole. Then, like a baseborn coward, he gave it a thick kiss, smack on the spot right near the hole. And so he got what he deserved. The lady turned around, and the knight said to her: "Fair sir, now tell me your name, and then you may go away content." "Sir knight," she said, "my name will never be hidden. There has never been one like it invented. None of my relatives bear it. I am called Beranger Longbottom, who puts all cowards to shame."

Then, having finished her business, she returned home. As soon as she could, she took off her armor and she sent for a knight whom she loved and held dear. She brought him softly into her chamber and hugged and kissed him. Now behold, the knight returns from the woods! The lady, who feared him not at all, did not deign to stir for his sake, but made her lover sit down by her side.

This baseborn knight, in great horror, came into the chamber. Know that he wasn't pleased at all when he saw his wife with her lover. At once he said: "Lady, you serve me dishonorably to bring a man in here. By my oath, you will pay for it!"

"Be quiet," said the lady, "you low fellow! Be careful not to say another word about this! For if you denounce me, by the Holy Ghost, I will complain of your wrongdoings out of spite, and you will turn out a jealous cuckold." "And to whom, by your leave," said he, "will you complain?" "To whom?" said she. "To your dear fellow in arms who only a little while ago held you in his power, to Lord Beranger Longbottom, who will put you to shame."

When the knight heard what she said, he was seized by great shame and rage. But he did not dare contradict her; he felt that he was vanquished and reduced to naught. And she who was neither a fool nor baseborn had everything her own way. For as the saying goes: *When the shepherd is weak, the wolf shits wool.*

"Bérengier au Lonc Cul" is one of the finest examples of the fabliau put to the service of satire, a sort of *Bourgeois Gentilhomme* of the thirteenth century. Though of low birth, the "knight" of the story is able, because of his father's money, to marry into a noble family. But what a discrepancy between the ideals of a true knight and those of this upstart! Given to inaction and an inordinate love of cakes and cream, the knight despises the common folk. He becomes insufferable during his brief hour of glory. But he is equally ready to grovel and whine when beside himself with fear, and is twice humiliated in a manner as vile as his extraction. Imagine a knight taking an oath *not* to do battle! "Beranger" well expresses the scorn which the nobility must have felt for the pretentions of a peasant parvenu.

Although the spirit of the tale is unmistakably Western and medieval, the nucleus of the story itself—called, in the terminology of the folklorists, the "shameful, or misdirected, kiss"—is as old as mankind and may well have originated in India. There are early forms of the story preserved in Greek and Mongol, the latter in the *Siddhi-Kûr* (*Book of Magic Spells*), dating from between the thirteenth and the fifteenth centuries. In the sixteenth century the tale was retold in a version which inspired an anecdote in *Roger Bontemps en Belle Humeur* (*Good-Humored Roger Bontemps*), printed in Cologne in 1708. Barthélemy Imbert put it into modern French verse in 1778.

The theme of the kissed rump is used in many other medieval tales, the most famous of which is Chaucer's "Miller's Tale."

The prologue states that the author of this fabliau was a certain Garin, about whom no information survives. Possibly he was the same Garin whose name is found associated with six other fabliaux, among them "The Knight Who Conjured Voices."

Edition: Rychner, II, 100–109.

THE PETTICOAT

by Jean de Condé

There are those who take more delight in hearing
jests and sly mockeries than they do in sermons. Therefore I
am often asked to write of light matters, and I should like
now to tell a true tale about a remarkable and quick-witted
piece of deception. But had someone discovered this fine deceit and the way it was devised, the lady of our tale would
surely have been in a fine mess.

There was once a lady, the wife of a merchant, who, without her husband's knowing it, took a lover, a young and
handsome squire. One night as he lay in bed with her (for
her husband was not at home) the merchant returned quietly

and softly lit a candle, with so little stir that nobody knew he was there. The wife, who lay side by side with her lover and held him in her arms, was not expecting such a guest. And the merchant, who knew nothing of this and suspected nothing, came straight into the chamber with the candle in his hand.

The wife was astonished when she saw the candle and sat up in terror, for she thought she had been betrayed. The squire, cheated of his pleasure, did not know what to say or do but duck under the covers and lie there trembling with fear and rage.

"Alas!" cried the wife. "Who is there? God and the sweet Virgin help me! Who can it be? My husband! Oh, how this terrible man has frightened me! I've almost lost my wits! Nice people don't come home like this, to spy on their wives. You've frightened me to death!"

"Be quiet," said the merchant. "Don't be afraid. Calm yourself, sweet sister, for never has it been in my heart to come home to spy on you, nor have I ever had any idea that I could catch you in some wickedness. So be easy, don't let this upset you." And he sat down at the foot of the bed. The heart of the squire under the covers began to pound, and he shook and trembled like an omelet over the fire. The merchant comforted his wife, who was so deathly pale that he didn't know what to do for her or how to reassure her.

"Sister," he said, "I have done wrong in this, but forgive me my fault, for I have never suspected you of anything." And his wife replied: "Then tell me, if you had found a man here by my side, and no mistake about it, what would you have done? Would you have allowed such a thing to pass?"

The merchant answered: "With this sword I would have cut off his head, and I would have killed you beside him."

Then the wife, who was a very clever woman and quick-witted when the occasion required it, laughed aloud and said to her husband: "You don't know what I would have done or how I would have defended myself. Why, I would have scarcely been afraid." She took her petticoat off the bed and threw it over her husband's head and held it there about his neck and face and so blinded the fool. Then she kicked her lover, who was trembling with anguish, all naked out of the bed, and he with a naked blade in his hand with which he had meant to defend himself and, if he could, to sell his life dearly. The lady held the merchant tight and laughed aloud and fooled with him, while the squire ran out of the room naked as he was. He would not be caught today.

"So I would have held you tight," said the lady, waiting for her chance to let him go, "until I had sent him on his way." And when she saw that her husband had no intention of doing her harm or injury, she took away the petticoat and left off her game. "Now he has escaped," she said. "He will not be caught today. Run after him! He is getting away!"

Have you ever heard of a neater trick? It was a beautiful one and a graceful one, full of cunning and sly malice. And she used it to great advantage, for through that trick she prevented a great misfortune.

When she had worked her purpose, the wife's heart was easy and at rest. She was joyous and happy. And her husband too, who took it all as a joke, was happy. The two of them had a great deal of fun together. And so it ended without more ado.

I do not know what else to say of this matter: one needn't

worry about her hiding the squire's clothes, for if she could carry out such a trick, the clothes would not present her with much difficulty. Truly I know no more about it, and so I end my tale here.

"Le Pliçon" introduces the stock fabliau figures of the sly and unscrupulous adulteress and her oafish husband. The nucleus of this fabliau comes from the lore of India, where it is found in the fourteenth-century *Hitopadesa* (*Book of Good Counsel*). It appears in both Roman and Greek antiquity, notably, at least in outline, in Aristophanes' *Thesmophoriazusae*. A variation of the fable served in the Middle Ages, in Tale 122 of the *Gesta Romanorum* (*Deeds of the Romans*), as a Christian allegory and was retold by Petrus Alphonsi in the eighth tale of the *Disciplina Clericalis* (*Instruction for the Clergy;* early twelfth century), the French translation of which, "Le Velous" ("The Velvet"), can be considered a fabliau. It is found in the works of many of the Italian novelists, in German in both Von der Hagen's *Gesammtabenteuer* (*Collected Tales;* 1850) and in the third tale of Wilhelm Kirchhof's *Wendunmuth* (1563), and in Henri Estienne's *Apologie pour Hérodote* (*Apology for Herodotus;* 1566), to list only a few of the many analogues. In most of these versions the petticoat is absent, and the lady covers her lover's escape by pretending to treat an injured eye of her husband.

A biographical note on Jean de Condé follows "The Beaten Path."

Edition: August Scheler, *Dits et Contes de Baudouin de Condé et de Son Fils Jean de Condé.* 3 vols. (Brussels, 1866). II, 127–131.

THE
PEASANT
DOCTOR

There was once a rich peasant who was very avaricious and stingy. He was never without a plow, which he worked himself with the aid of a mare and an old nag; he had plenty of meat and bread and wine and whatever else he needed. But his friends and everyone else found fault with him because he had no wife. He said that he would take a good one willingly, if he could find one; and they said that they would search until they found the best one they could.

In that country there lived a knight, an old man and a widower. He had a daughter who was a very beautiful and well-mannered young lady. But, because he lacked money, the knight could not find anyone who would ask for his daughter's hand, although he would very willingly have married her off, she being of an age and disposition to wed. The peasant's friends went to this knight and asked for his daughter's hand on behalf of the peasant, who had so much gold and silver, such an abundance of grain, and such great plenty of linens. He gave her to them straightway and agreed to this marriage. The daughter, who was motherless and very dutiful, did not dare oppose her father, and so she agreed to do as he wished. So the peasant, as soon as he could, made his wedding and took to wife this girl, who was much grieved at the marriage and who, if she dared, would have done anything not to go through with it.

After the wedding had taken place and all that went with it, the peasant was not long in thinking that he had made a bad bargain. For it did not suit his trade at all to have a knight's daughter at home when he went out to plow. A young lord, for whom every day is a holiday, can go strolling down the street; perhaps when he was away from the house, the priest would come to visit, today, tomorrow, and the day after, until he had seduced his wife. Nor would she ever love him or hold him dearer than two loaves of bread.

"Alas, poor wretch that I am!" he said. "Now I don't know where to look for advice; for it's no use being sorry now." Then he began to think how he could keep what he feared from happening. "My God!" he cried, "if I should beat her in the morning when I get up, she would weep all day and I could go and work my land. I'm sure that as long as she wept no one would come courting her. In the evening when I come back, I shall ask her forgiveness, for the love of God. I shall make her happy in the evening, but in the morning she shall sulk. I'll take leave of her then, when I have had a bite to eat."

Then the peasant asked for something to eat, and his wife

hastened to bring it to him. They did not have salmon or partridge, but bread and wine they had, and fried eggs and cheese in great abundance, which the peasant had stored up. And when the table was cleared, with the palm of his hand, which was large and wide, the peasant struck his wife across the face so hard that he left the marks of his fingers there. Then this churl, who was very strong, seized her by the hair and beat her just as if she had deserved it. Then he went straight to his fields, and his wife remained there weeping.

"Alas!" she said. "What shall I do? And how shall I be comforted? I do not know any more what to say. My father indeed betrayed me when he gave me to that baseborn fellow. Was I afraid that I would die of hunger? Surely I must have had madness in my heart when I agreed to such a marriage. God, why did my mother die!" So pitifully did she lament that everyone who came to see her turned away again.

Thus did she grieve until the sun had set and the peasant returned home. Then he fell at her feet and begged her forgiveness for God's sake. "Know," he said, "that the Adversary did this to me; it was he who made me do violence. See here, I give you my word that I will never raise a hand to you again. I am grieved and distressed that I beat you." This stinking peasant pleaded so much that his wife pardoned him and gave him the supper which she had prepared; and when he had had enough to eat, they went to bed in peace. But in the morning this stinkard once again beat his wife so hard that he almost crippled her. Then he went again to plow his fields. The lady began to weep. "Alas!" said she. "What shall I do and how shall I be comforted? I can see that evil has befallen me. Has my husband ever been beaten? Not he, he does not know what blows are. If he did, not for all the world would he give me so many of them."

While she was sorrowing thus, behold, two of the king's messengers, each on a white palfrey, came riding toward her. They greeted her in the king's name and asked her to give them something to eat, for they were in great need of food. Willingly she gave them something, and then she asked them: "Where are you going and where do you come from? And tell me, what are you looking for?" One of them answered: "Madam, in faith, we are messengers of the king, who has sent us to look for a physician. We must go over to England." "What for?" said the wife. "Because Mistress Aude, the king's daughter, is sick. It is eight days since she was able to eat or drink, for a fishbone is stuck in her throat. Now, the king is very grieved; if he loses her he will never be happy again."

Then the lady said: "You will not go as far as you think; for my husband, I assure you, is a fine physician. Really, he knows more about medicines and how to judge truly from urine than ever Hippocrates did." "Lady, are you joking?" "I have no wish to joke," she said, "but my husband is of such a humor that he won't do anything for anybody unless he is first beaten soundly." And they answered: "Well, it's not likely he'll remain behind for lack of a beating. Lady, where can we find him?" "You'll find him in the fields. When you come out of this courtyard, follow right along the course of the brook on the other side of that abandoned road, and the first plow you come to is ours. Go," she said. "To Saint Peter the apostle I commend you."

And they went riding off until they found the peasant. They greeted him in the king's name, and then, without further ado, they said to him: "Come immediately to speak to the king." "What for?" said the peasant. "Because of the wisdom that's in you. There is not such a fine doctor in this country. We have come a great distance to find you." When the peasant heard himself called a doctor, his blood began to boil, and he said that where such things were concerned he didn't know beans from onions. "Now then," said the first messenger, "what are we waiting for?" And the second one said: "You know that before he says or does anything worthwhile he expects to be beaten." The first one struck him on the ear, and the second struck him square in the back with a big thick staff he had; they beat him shamefully. Then they mounted him on a horse, his face to the tail, and led him to the king.

The king came to meet them and said to them: "Have you found anything?" "Yes, sire," they said together; and the peasant trembled with fear. One of the messengers spoke up and told the king about the peasant's peculiar foibles: that he was full of trickery and would do nothing for anyone if he were not beaten soundly first. "What a wretched physician we have here," said the king. "Never before have I heard tell of such a one." And one of the servants said: "Let him be beaten then, if that's the way it is. I am ready. You have only to say the word and I shall give him what he deserves." The king addressed the peasant. "Master doctor," he said, "listen. I shall send for my daughter, for she is in great need of a cure." The peasant cried for mercy. "For God's sake, sire," he said, "before God, who does not lie, I tell you that I know nothing of medicine, nor am I of the physician's trade." And the king said: "What wonders do I hear! Beat him for me!" His servants, who went willingly about their work, seized the peasant; and when he felt the blows, he thought he was going mad. "Mercy!" he began to cry. "I will cure her at once."

The girl was brought into the hall, all pale and flushed, and the peasant wondered how he could cure her, for he well knew that he must either do so or die. Then he thought that if he wanted to cure her and save her, what he had to do was say or do something to make her laugh; and that would make the bone jump out of her throat, for she had not swallowed it down into her body. So he said to the king: "Have a fire made in that room which lies apart. You will see what I shall do and how, if it please God, I shall cure her."

The king had a roaring fire made; the squires and servants hopped to it and quickly lit the fire where the king had ordered it. And the maiden came and sat by the fire on a stool which they had brought for her. The peasant took off his breeches and stripped himself all naked. Then he stretched out across the fire and scratched and curried himself. He had long nails and a tough skin, and know, you couldn't find a better scratcher from here to Saumur. The maiden, when she saw this, in spite of all the pain she felt, wanted to laugh; and she strained so hard that the bone flew out of her throat and onto the coals. At once the peasant put on his clothes, took up the bone, and ran out of the room in great joy. When he saw the king, he cried out loud: "Sire, your daughter is cured! Here is the bone, thanks to God!"

The king was overjoyed and said: "Now know that I love you above all things. Now you shall have robes and linens." "Thank you, sire," said the peasant, "but I don't want them and I can't stay. I must go back home." "That you shall not do," said the king. "You will be my physician and my friend." "Thanks, sire, but by Saint German, there was no bread at my house when I left yesterday morning. I was to have gone and got some at the mill." The king called two boys. "Beat him for me," he said, "and he'll stay." The boys leapt on him at once and began to beat him. When the peasant felt the blows on his arms and on his legs and on his back, he began to cry for mercy: "I'll stay, let me be!"

So the peasant remained at court. His hair and whiskers were trimmed, and he wore a robe of scarlet. But how embarrassed he was when the sick of that country, more than eighty of them, I believe, came before the king on a certain holiday, and each of them told his misfortune. The king called the peasant. "Doctor," he said, "take care of these people; do it quickly and cure them for me." "Sire," the peasant said, "may God help me, there are too many of them. I can't accomplish so much or cure them all." The king called two boys, and each of them picked up a rod for they well knew why the king called them. When the peasant saw them coming, his blood began to freeze. "Mercy!" he cried. "I will cure them immediately."

The peasant asked for some wood, of which there was more than enough, and a fire was built in the hall, which he kindled himself. He assembled all the sick people, and then he said to the king: "Sire, you must leave the room and all those who are not sick." The king left the hall very willingly, he and all his household. Then the peasant said to the sick people: "My lords, by the God who made me, there is a great deal to cure you of. I do not think I can do it all. I shall select the sickest one and put him on that fire; I shall burn him up there, and the others will benefit from this, for all who swallow the powder of the man who has been burned will be cured immediately." They looked at one another, and the most hunchbacked or dropsical one among them would not admit, for all of Normandy, that he was the sickest one there. The peasant said to the first: "I see that you have grown very weak. You are the worst afflicted of the lot." "No, thank you, my lord, I am quite healthy. I am relieved of the great pain which I suffered for a long time. I wouldn't lie to you about it in any way." "Go out then," said the peasant. "What were you looking for here?" The sick man made for the door, and when he came out the king asked him: "Are you cured?" "Yes, sire, I am sounder than an apple. You have a very worthy man in that doctor."

But why should I make a long story of it? Not one of them, large or small, would agree, for all the world, to be thrown into the fire; they chose rather to go away just as if they had been cured. And when the king saw them, he was beside himself with joy. He said to the peasant: "I wonder at how you cured them so quickly!" "Thank you, sire," said the peasant. "I cast a spell on them. I know a spell that is worth more than ginger or setwall." And the king said: "Now you may go home whenever you like, and you will take with you money and horses, both palfreys and war steeds. And when I send for you again, you will do what I want. You will be my dear good friend, and I shall love you more than anyone in the land. But don't be foolish any more and cause yourself to be beaten, for it is a shame to strike you." "Thank you, sire," said the peasant. "I am your man evening and morning, and so I shall be as long as I live. Nor will I ever go back on my word."

He took his leave of the king and joyfully returned home. Never had there been a richer landholder. He no longer went to the plow, nor did he ever again beat his wife; rather, he loved and cherished her. So it happened as I have told you: because of his wife and his own cunning, he was a good physician without learning.

The fabliau of "Le Vilain Mire" consists in reality of three distinct narrative motifs artistically welded into a single tale. These motifs include those of the simpleton who must be beaten to make him accomplish some action, of the fake doctor who heals through stratagems, and of the physician who empties the hospital by threatening to kill the most sick to heal the others. Superimposed on the finished product are a situation and an attitude common to the fabliaux: conjugal strife and class satire. The first two plot motifs are widely extant. In sermon literature they are found in the 237th *exemplum* of the thirteenth-century *Sermones Vulgares* (*Common Sermons*) of Jacques de Vitry (ca. 1178–1240), from which they were adapted in the *Compilatio Singularis Exemplorum* (*Unique Compilation of Exempla;* end of the thirteenth century), in the *Exempla* (1250) of Etienne de Bourbon, and in the fourteenth century in a French version in the *Contes Moralisés* (*Moral Tales;* ca. 1340) of Nicole Bozon. Later, the motifs figured as Tale 73 in the fourth book of the *Mensa Philosophica* (*The Philosophers' Banquet;* 1475), an interesting treatise on the proper form for a philosophers' dinner party. Among the numerous versions that appeared after the Renaissance, both motifs are found as separate tales in the *Sérées* (*Evening Tales;* 1534) of Guillaume Bouchet (Nos. 10 and 30). They have even been recorded as a folk tale from the Basque country. But it was Molière who made the story famous in his comedy *Le Médecin Malgré Lui* (*The Doctor in Spite of Himself*)—most probably inspired by an Italian farce entitled *Arlecchino Medico Volante* (*Harlequin, the Wandering Doctor*).

The third motif, like the first two, is frequently found as a separate tale. It stems ultimately from the East, where it is preserved in the *Sukasaptati* (*Sixty Tales of the Parrot,* ca. second century A.D.). Some of its more well-known occurrences in Western literature are in a second *exemplum* from Jacques de Virty (No. 254), in the German collection *Till Eulenspiegel* (No. 15; early sixteenth century), in Poggio's (1380–1459) *Liber Facetiarum* (*Book of Pleasantries;* No. 190), and in the sixteenth-century jest book "Certayne Conceytes and Jests" (No. 2).

Edition: Carl Zipperling, *Das Altfranzösische Fablel du Vilain Mire* (Halle, 1912).

WILLIAM AND THE FALCON

He who deals in tales should not neglect any that are worth telling. I have one to tell now.

There was once a handsome youth named William, so debonair that you might search through twenty kingdoms and not find his equal for beauty. He was not a knight, but a squire, and had spent seven whole years in the service of a lord castellan without receiving the reward of his service, which was knighthood and the arms of a knight. He was not over-eager to become a knight, and the reason for this was that his heart had been moved by love for the wife of his lord. He had fallen in love so deeply with that lady that he could not bring himself to leave her, although the lady herself had no idea that the squire loved her so desperately.

If she had known of his love, she would have been careful never to speak so much as a word to him. For these women, so wicked-wise in the ways of love, when they know that they have conquered a man's heart, although he should tear his face in anguish, always choose not to speak to him. I am not lying when I say that they would much rather go play with some broken-down vagabond than with one who loves them. But such a woman, if she has any love at all for the man, does ill to treat him that way. May God curse the lady who behaves so, for she is guilty of a great sin; when once she has entangled a man in those wicked bonds from which he may hardly escape, she ought not to be so base as to leave him thus without help, whose thoughts can take no other direction. But let me return to my tale.

This William, then, had set his thoughts and his love on this lady. He was in the power of the God of Love, who made his life a martyrdom. To tell you some little part of that lady's great beauty—no flower of the fields, neither the May rose nor the lily flower, could compare with her. If you searched throughout the world, you could not find a fairer woman, not even in the kingdom of Castile, where live the prettiest ladies in the world. Let me try, in as delicate a manner as I can, to trace here some description of her beauty. This lady when adorned in her robes was more charming, more elegant, and more gracious than is a new-molted falcon or a sparrow hawk or a gay parrot. Her tunic was of purple; her gown was sown with golden stars and had a lining of ermine not the least bit worn; her cloak, its collar trimmed with black and gray sable, was neither too long nor too wide.

And in describing those beauties with which God had endowed her woman's body and her face, I pray that my heart may so work that not one word of falsehood may remain in my description. Her hair when she had let it down would seem to one who beheld it to be made all of gold, it was so yellow and so bright. Her forehead was shining and smooth, as though it had been finished by hand; her eyebrows were brown, and her eyes, wide spaced, were bright and smiling, large and sparkling. Her nose was fine and straight; and more pleasing in her face was that rose on white so prettily set between cheek and ear than are gules on silver. Her mouth was scarlet and looked like a corn cockle, it was so vermeil and so small; and her chin was so lovely that I do not know how to describe it. Also, her throat and bosom seemed made of ice or crystal, they were so clear and shining; and on her chest were hung two little breasts like little apples. But what more should I say? God had made in her a marvel of marvels; never had her equal been seen. Nature in making this lady had brought all her powers to work and all her wisdom, so that for a long time afterward she was left impoverished. But I cannot speak more of her beauty.

One day this lord castellan, in order to enhance his worth and his reputation, went off to a tourney to a far country, and he stayed there a long time, for he was very rich and powerful. He took with him a great number of knights and servants, and in his retinue were only the worthiest knights, of whom the most cowardly were brave men. William, greatly troubled by love, had no wish to go to the tourney, but preferred to stay at home; and so he remained at the castle. The God of Love had so surprised him that he did not know what to do or where to turn.

And of the evil that so oppressed him he lamented thus to himself: "Alas, poor wretch! I was born in an evil hour! I have given my love there where I may never hope to see my desires granted. Too long indeed have I kept what is in my heart hidden from her. It is madness to languish thus all my days and she to know nothing of it. It is only right that I tell her of my love; it would be foolish not to tell her soon. At this rate I might as well love all the ladies beyond the seas. You will tell her! But tell her what? You do not have enough courage to dare tell her what you suffer for her. But I will, I swear! But it is so hard to make a beginning. Yet I will tell her how much I love her, even though it avail me nothing."

And William answered himself thus: "I am hot and burning with love; yet when it comes to taking the first step, I do not know what to do and am half tempted to turn back."

But William then took courage, and bravely, with no sign of reluctance, strode into the hall. All quietly he pushed open the lady's door and entered her chamber. As chance would have it, he found the lady alone there, her maids-in-waiting having retired into another room, where they were making merry while embroidering a lion or a leopard on a piece of silk, which was to be the device of some knight.

William was not to be put off. There was the lady seated on her bed; no man of woman born has seen a fairer creature. William was overcome with her beauty; and when he saw his opportunity he was eager to seize it. He gave the lady a sweet look and greeted her. She was not the least bit dismayed, but smiled at him prettily and, laughing, returned his greeting.

"William," she said, "come here."

"Willingly, lady," said he with a sigh.

"Come, sit down here, my dear sweet friend."

The lady was not aware of the state of William's heart when she called him her dear friend; for if she had known it she would never have spoken thus. William sat down on the bed beside the beautiful lady, and the two of them made merry together and laughed and spoke of many things, until at last William gave a great sigh and said:

"Lady, I pray you listen to me and give me some advice on a matter I shall speak to you of."

"Very well," said she. "Speak."

"Lady," he said, "if a scholar or a knight should fall in love, or a merchant or a youth—let us say a squire, even—or any one of those; and let us say that he falls in love with a lady or with a girl, a queen or a countess or a young virgin —let her be what she will, of high rank or of low; and if he has loved her for seven whole years and kept his love concealed all that time and still does not dare tell her how much he has suffered for her; and now he has the chance to tell her what is in his heart, if only he had the courage to do so —well then, tell me what you think: has he acted wisely or foolishly in so concealing his love? That is what I should like to know."

"William," the lady said, "for my part, I shall tell you just what I believe. I do not hold him wise who does not reveal his heart when he has the chance to speak to his love. If she will not return his love, surely he is very foolish to continue to suffer for her. But if Love has so constrained him that he cannot escape, then I would advise him certainly to tell her of his passion. Love demands boldness. I shall give you a good judgment: he whom Cupid has caught in his net should not be a coward, but should act confidently and boldly. If ever I should fall in love, I swear by Saint Denis I would tell my love bravely. And so I would advise him to do; if she decides to love him, she will do so."

William groaned and answered her, sighing: "Lady, look then on him who for so long has borne the pain of loving you. Lady, I dare not tell you of the grief and pain I have suffered these many years. It has cost me much to reveal it.

My sweet lady, I yield myself to you. I would be in your service and put myself wholly at your command. Lady, heal me of the great wound I have in my body. There is no one alive who can cure me, except you alone; of this I am certain. I am all yours and always have been yours and always will be. No man could live in greater pain than I have done. Lady, I ask that you grant me the gift of your love, for which I am in such distress." The lady heard well what he said but held his declaration in contempt and told him at once that she did not care a penny for what he had said.

"William," she said, "is this a joke? I will not love you. Go make fun of someone else. I swear I have never heard such nonsense as you have spoken. If you speak to me again of this, as God loves me I shall not fail to bring shame on you. I understand nothing of what love means nor of what you ask of me. Go away, good sir! Go on, get out of here! And do not come again into my presence! My lord will be very pleased no doubt to hear of this. Surely, as soon as he returns I shall tell him what language you dared to use to me. I cannot tell you how mad and stupid I think you are. May he go hang who brought you here! Good sir, go away!"

When William heard this he was in great dismay, as you may imagine, and he was sorry for what he had said. He could answer her nothing, he was so wretched and astounded.

"Alas!" he said. "I am betrayed. Now I remember that saying: The messenger who brings bad news comes always too early."

But Love exhorted and commanded him to speak to her again and not to leave her thus.

"Lady," he said, "it weighs heavy on me that you will grant me no other favor than this. But you are guilty of a great sin, when once you have taken me in your bonds, to seek to do me further harm. Kill me if you wish. I have asked you for your love; and that gift I will have on these terms: that I shall never again take food until you give me your love, for which I live in such distress."

"By the holy Homer!" said the lady. "You will have to fast indeed. For if you do not intend to eat until you have my love, you will go without food until the new-sown wheat is harvested."

Then William left her chamber; he did not take leave of her. He had his bed made and lay down in it. But, when he had lain down, he took little rest. For three whole days he lay in bed, and he neither ate nor drank. The fourth day approached and still he lay thus. The lady remained haughty toward him and did not deign to look at him, although she knew well that he was fasting and would not eat the least thing.

William's pains never ceased but tormented him day and night. It was little wonder that he grew pale and thin, for he did not eat and he lay always awake in great distress. When his eyes moved a little, he imagined that he saw his lovely lady and that he felt her in his arms lying in his bed and that he took his delight with her. As long as that vision lasted he was much comforted, for he seemed to embrace her and kiss her. But when the vision faded, then he trembled and sighed and stretched out his arms but found nothing in them. He is mad who pursues madness. He would look everywhere in his bed for his lady, and, when he did not find her, he struck himself on the face and breast. The God of Love held him fast. Love held him in bonds. Love kept him in this great torment. He wished that his visions might continue, but Love summoned him back to cold and trembling.

And now I wish to speak about the lord, who was on his

way back from his tourney, bringing with him a great company of men. He sent a squire ahead to inform his lady that her lord was returning and that he brought fifteen prisoners with him, rich and powerful knights, and other great booty also. When the lady heard the news, she was full of joy. All glad and happy, she had the hall readied and good food prepared and made all the arrangements for the coming of her lord.

Poor William was in great distress; and it occurred to the lady that she should go to him and tell him of her lord's return from the lists and ask him why he was so silly as to persist in not eating. She went straight to his bedside; but, though she stood there a great while, William did not see her. Then she called him by name, but he seemed removed to another world. She cried a little louder and touched him with her finger. When at last he heard her, he trembled; when he felt her touch him, he broke out into a sweat; and when he saw her he greeted her.

"Lady," he said, "you are as welcome to me as health and cure. Lady, before God I beseech you, have pity on me."

And the lady replied: "William, on my word, you will never have my pity in the form you want it. You have ill requited the favors of my lord in making advances to his wife. Is that the sort of love you bear toward him? The day will never come that you will possess me. But you are acting very foolishly, William, in not eating. If you kill yourself this way, your soul will be lost. I will never give you that gift you ask for. You would do better to get up, for my lord is coming back from the tourney. On my word, he may be here at any moment. And as God may keep me, he shall know why you are lying here, and you will not escape his anger."

"Lady," said William, "all this is useless. If you had my

limbs cut off, I would not eat. I have this great burden on my shoulders which I cannot put down. I cannot keep from loving you, though I fast or though I die. Lady, do whatever you wish."

Thereupon she left him, without granting his wish, and went into the hall, which was richly adorned, the tables all in their places and covered with cloths. Then the food was brought in: bread and wines and great joints roasted on the spit. The knights entered and sat down at table. They were served more richly than I can tell here. The lord and lady dined together, and the castellan looked about the hall for William, very much surprised that he did not come to wait on him.

"Lady," he said, "in good faith, can you tell me why William has not come to greet me?"

"He has got too shy," said the lady. "Truthfully, he has fallen ill of a malady for which, I believe, he will never find a remedy."

"Now by Saint Denis," said the castellan, "I am very sorry to hear he is so ill."

But if he had known the cause of William's illness and why he lay in bed, William would never have got up again. He does not know yet. But this is a ticklish situation, and I am afraid that he will find out only too soon. If William does not eat soon, the lady will tell the castellan everything, and William will lose his head.

When the knights had risen from table, the lady could delay no longer. She took her husband by his cloak and said: "My lord, I am surprised that you do not go to see William. You ought to find out what disease he is suffering from. As for me, I think he may be malingering."

And so they went together to William's chamber, where they found William sunk in a dream and crying on death to come and take him quickly, for he could no longer bear such pain and agony. The castellan, like the gracious lord he was, kneeled down at William's feet and gently questioned him.

"William," he said, "my dear friend, what illness has so overwhelmed you? Tell me now, how do you feel?"

"My lord," said William, "I am not well. I have a great pain that comes and goes through my limbs and my head, and I fear it will never leave me."

"And can you not eat or drink?"

"No, I cannot eat of any food that God has made."

At this the lady could no longer keep from speaking, even if she had been flayed alive for it.

"My lord," she said, "this is all vain talk. Let William say what he likes, I know what illness he has and where it hurts him. Believe me, it is not a pain in his finger. No, it is a disease that makes those who have it sweat and sometimes also tremble."

Then she turned to William and said: "William, so help me God, if you do not eat now, the time is drawing near when you will never eat again."

"I can bear no more," said William, "say what you will. You are my lady and he is my lord, but I cannot eat, not even if you should have my arms and my legs cut off."

"My lord," she said then, "see now how foolish William is. Not long ago, while you were away on your tourney, William, who lies here ill, came to me in my chamber."

"In your chamber, lady? Why did he do that? What did he want of you there in your chamber?"

"My lord, I shall tell you truly. William, will you still eat nothing? In a moment, I shall tell my lord of your great shame and dishonor."

"No, by my faith!" said William. "Believe me, I shall never eat again."

Then the lord castellan said to his wife: "On my soul! you must think me mad or a fool not to lay a stick alongside your ribs!"

"Hold on!" said she. "Enough! I swear I will tell you everything!" And to William she said: "Will you eat, William? Or shall I tell?"

William sighed and answered her piteously, as one who feels great anguish: "I will not eat at any price, unless the pain in my heart is first assuaged."

Then did the lady take pity on him and answered her husband: "My lord, William, whom you see here, asked me for your falcon, and I would not give it to him. For, indeed, what right have I to meddle with your birds?"

Then said the castellan: "That does not please me. For I would rather that all my birds, falcons, goshawks, and sparrow hawks, were dead than that William should fast a single day."

"My lord," said the lady, "then give it to him, since it is your wish. If he wants it, he shall not go without it because of me. William, on my faith, since my husband grants it to you, it would be mean of me to deny it to you."

When William heard her words, he was happier and more joyous than any man could say. At once he got up and put on his clothes. His illness no longer afflicted him. As soon as he was dressed and shod, he went straight to the hall. And, when the lady saw him come in, she heaved a sigh, for Cupid had shot an arrow into her; now she too must take her part in love, go hot and cold and often change color.

The castellan said to William: "You are a mad boy to take such a liking to my falcon. You have worried me a great deal.

For I don't know another man, be he wise or foolish, a noble prince or a count, to whom I would give my falcon, whether in return for service or as a favor." Then he said to one of his retainers: "Go bring my falcon."

His man brought it quickly to him, and the lord took it by its jesses and gave it to William, who thanked him heartily.

"Well," said the lady, "now you have a falcon; and two ducats are worth more than a gold noble."

And that was well said and had a double meaning; for he would have two things instead of one, and that before a day had passed: the falcon which he had wanted so badly and the love of the lady, which he treasured more than any other delight.

So in this fabliau I have provided a new lesson for those young men who carry on the game of love and shown them that when they fall in love with ladies of great beauty they must press their suit boldly and not give up even if at first their ladies refuse them, but persist until they are softened by pleading. They must do as William did, who put his whole heart and body into his suit and so came to great joy, as you have heard here. And may God grant as much joy, without delay and without fail, to all those who suffer pain and grief for love's sake. And He will do so, if only they do not lose heart.

Here ends my tale.

"Guillaume au Faucon" is one of the most charming of the fabliaux to have survived. Its humor is subtle and urbane, and it seems closer in tone to the short lay or courtly romance than to the fabliau. Nevertheless, it belongs in the latter genre because it is above all a humorous story. It may be thought of as a little satire on the conventions of courtly love.

Students of the fabliaux have been unable to find a single source or early analogue for "William," although the devices of the courtly love tale—sickness, the wish for death, and the miraculous cure—were all commonplaces in the tales of the twelfth and thirteenth centuries. It is possible that the portrait of William inspired that of Damian in Chaucer's "Merchant's Tale." This young squire, like William, was deathly ill but made a swift recovery on the promise of the fulfillment of his desires.

The author of the fabliau is unknown, but dialectal characteristics would indicate that he was from the region around Paris.

Edition: Reid, pp. 83–98.

THE WOMAN WHO HANGED
HER HUSBAND'S BODY

by Marie de France

The tale is written of a man who died and was
buried. His wife mourned with great sorrow night and day
on his grave. Nearby there was a thief who had been hanged
for his misdeeds. A certain knight took him down (he was a
relative of his) and buried him. And it was announced
throughout the country that whoever had removed the thief's
body would suffer the same fate: if he were caught, he would
be hanged.

The knight did not know where to turn for deliverance, for many people knew that the thief was his relation. He went straight to the cemetery where the good woman was mourning so hard for her husband. He spoke to her fondly, told her to take heart, and said that he would be very happy if she would love him. The good woman looked at him and grew joyful. She promised to grant his desire.

Then the knight told her of the misfortune that had befallen him because of the thief he had taken down from the gallows. If she could not help him, he would have to leave the country. The good woman replied: "Let us dig up my husband who is buried here and hang him in the other's place. No one will know the difference. The living, to whom one looks for joy, must be saved by the dead."

From this lesson we can learn how much trust the dead may place in the living. So false and frivolous is the world.

"De Vidua"—Marie de France gave her fabliaux Latin titles—is a retelling of the ageless story of woman's inconstancy. It is the famous tale of the "Matron of Ephesus," from Petronius' *Satyricon* (first century A.D.), which was repeated in a fable of Phaedrus, from where it passed into the tenth-century Latin *Romulus*. In Old French a longer version is found in a fabliau of the latter half of the thirteenth century, "The Woman Who Fornicated on Her Husband's Tomb" ("Celle Qui Se Fist Foutre sur la Fosse de Son Mari," translated in *Playboy Magazine*, March 1958, as "The Poisonous Knight"); this fabliau was probably the source of the story incorporated by Jehan Lefevre into his *Lamentations de Matheolus* (*Lamentations of Matthew;* 1370), a violent attack on women and marriage. Based on Petronius' tale are modern adaptations by La Fontaine and Saint-Evremond.

Edition: Karl Bartsch, *Chrestomathie de l'Ancien Français* (Leipzig, 1927), pp. 182–183.

THE MAN
WHO HAD
A QUARRELSOME WIFE

by Marie de France

A peasant who had married a very contrary-minded wife went for a walk with her one day in a pasture. The peasant remarked to his wife that he had never seen a pasture so evenly mowed. She quickly answered: "No, it wasn't mowed, it was done with a sharp scissors." The peasant said: "On the contrary, it was mowed." "No," said the woman, "clipped."

Then the peasant grew angry. "It is clear you are a fool," he said, "this grass was cut with a scythe. But you've always got to get your word in. Now I intend that my word shall prevail, and I am stubborn enough to make it do so." The peasant threw her down and cut out her tongue. Then he asked for her opinion: was the pasture mowed with a scythe or clipped with a scissors? Since she could not speak, she showed with her fingers that a scissors had cut it, and that no scythe had mown it.

By this tale I mean to show, as has been often proven, that when a fool speaks foolishness and someone comes along and speaks sense to him, the fool will not believe him but will grow angry; and, even when he knows he is wrong, he will try to make his lie prevail, which no one can do by remaining silent.

"De Homine et Uxore Litigiosa," again inspired by the *Romulus,* is a very well-known example of a type of tale of woman's obstinacy that appears in hundreds of forms, both popular and literary. The story is found in another fabliau, "Le Pré Tondu" ("The Clipped Meadow"; c. 1280), as well as in the thirteenth-century manuals of both Etienne de Bourbon and Jacques de Vitry. But the tale of the obstinate wife was better known under a slightly different form: a woman refuses to cease calling her husband lousy, and, as he lowers her into a well to punish her, she makes the gesture of squeezing a louse between her fingers. A good representative of this version is found in the *Liber Facetiarum* of Poggio, translated as "Of a Woman Who Insisted on Calling Her Husband Lousy" in *Wit and Wisdom of the Italian Renaissance* by Charles Speroni (Berkeley, 1964).

Edition: Karl Warnke, *Die Fabeln der Marie de France* (Halle, 1898), pp. 304–306.

Marie de France, whose literary activity dates from the second half of the twelfth century, was the first woman known to have written in the French language. What little is known of her life is gleaned from her three literary works that survive: *Les Lais* (*The Lays*), a collection of twelve narrative poems taken from the lyrics of the Breton minstrels; *Isopet* (*Fables*), adaptations into French verse from an Anglo-Saxon version of *Romulus;* and *Espurgatoire Saint Patriz* (*Purgatory of Saint Patrick*), an account of the visit of the legendary Irish saint to the other world. Although born in France, Marie lived most of her life in England. There she was doubtless in close association with the court of Henry II, to whom she dedicated *Les Lais*. Several years later she presented to William Longsword, Henry's bastard son, her collection of Aesopic fables, among which are found these two fabliaux. The *Espurgatoire* was composed toward the end of her career, certainly before 1189. Because of this sequence it has been suggested that her literary preoccupation evolved from the mundane spirit of *Les Lais* through the moralizing of *Isopet* to the strong religious concern found in her legend of the saint.

The two selections from *Isopet* included here are not, strictly speaking, fabliaux. The terseness of their narrative and the fact that they belong to a larger work of marked moralistic intention would seem to exclude them from that genre. But, unlike most of the other fables of the collection, they deal with real people and show the love of intrigue that is typical of the fabliau. Both anecdotes, moreover, are found elsewhere in more fully developed fabliau form. In the words of the medievalist Per Nykrog, Marie's tales represent "*fabliaux avant la lettre,*" and as such they have been included here in translation.

THE PRIEST'S BREECHES

by Jean de Condé

I have heard many tales of how priests have shamed
men and slept with their wives. Many merry tales have been
made on that theme, and I shall tell a new one.

Once, not very long ago, there lived in a certain town a
butcher whose wife loved a priest better than she did her
husband, for the priest knew better how to please her when
they met together secretly. The butcher, who knew nothing
of this, had decided to go to market one day with some
companions, his fellow tradesmen; and he got together the
money he needed so that he might set out the next day, for

he wanted to make an early start. His wife let the priest know that she could lie with him in peace, and the priest, who lusted after her, kept watch for the butcher's departure. The wife, who despised her husband, sent him off before daybreak. When he left the house, the priest, who was not far away, got into the lady's bed.

The butcher went to call for his friends, but they said: "Who has cast a spell on you? The cocks have not crowed yet. It is scarcely past midnight. Go back to bed if you please, for you can still get some good sleep in. You're too much of a worrier." The husband went back home, where his wife said: "Why have you come back? What do you want now?" "The others don't want to go yet," said her husband. The priest was all dismayed, but the wife told him not to worry but to lie quietly against the wall. And the butcher went back to sleep. The wife was well shared at least, for she had two men in her game: the priest lay on her right, and her husband snored on her left.

When it was near daybreak, the butcher's companions made ready and came to call for their friend. The butcher started up like a watchdog and got out of bed without delay. He reached down to the foot of the bed to get his breeches, but he was in such a hurry to join the friends who were waiting for him that he made a mistake and took the priest's breeches instead. He went out to meet his companions and set out for the market. The priest got back into bed and took his pleasure. And when it pleased him to get up, he put on the butcher's breeches and he felt the heavy purse in them. He went off saying: "I haven't gone far wrong, for I have come into money. Now I'll go drink, for I had no money of my own."

The others meanwhile had come to the market, where they looked about for some beasts to buy. The butcher bought one and at once went to put down his earnest money. But when he looked in the pocket of his breeches, where he thought to find his money, he found an empty purse with the priest's seal in it. There were a great many people about him, and he stood there as though he'd been whipped, shamed and sad at heart. "By the faith I owe Saint Thomas!" he said, "here's a very strange thing." A great laugh went up around him. The butcher was much embarrassed and seized with rage when he found the priest's seal. Now he had clear proof that the priest had lain with his wife. One of his companions said to him: "Comrade, what have you done with your breeches? That seal you have there is a true sign that the priest is the delight of your wife and a partner in your goods, for he has your purse filled with coin." The butcher was more at a loss than a sheep in the midst of ten wolves. And everyone cried: "Look at the cuckold!" He could not pay for the beast, and completely undone he returned home.

That is what happened to him. The news of it got abroad, and when the bishop heard of it, he forbade all priests to hang their seals on their breeches. And so I say to you in conclusion that priests have too much wiggle in their hips and thereby have brought many men to shame. I have told you many tales based on truth. Now I am silent, for I know no more.

"Les Braies le Priestre" vividly shows the anticlericalism and at the same time the antifeminism so prevalent in many of the fabliaux. Even the bishop is not spared, but is humorously charged with complicity in the irregularities of the priests of his diocese. The whole plot turns on an exchange of breeches that brings about the double undoing of the simple-minded butcher, a character who stands in striking contrast to his astute counterpart in "The Butcher of Abbeville."

The story told by Jean de Condé in "The Priest's Breeches" was circulated in various forms both before and after his own time. Its earliest known version, from the second century A.D., is the "Philetaerus and Myrmex" episode in Apuleius' *The Golden Ass*. Numerous analogous tales are found in several Italian writers of the fourteenth and fifteenth centuries—Sacchetti, Sabadino, Poggio Bracciolini—as well as in the *Orlando Innamorato* (*Roland in Love; 1487*) of Boiardo and in Henri Estienne's *Apologie pour Hérodote* (*Apology for Herodotus; 1566*), to mention only a few early examples.

The story was also exploited in dramatic form in the late medieval *Farce de Frère Guillebert* (*The Farce of Brother Guillebert*), and a close parallel to the tale is preserved in a second, anonymous fabliau called "Les Braies au Cordelier" ("The Franciscan's Breeches"), which carries the action further with a final insult. Confronted by the evidence, the wife hurriedly claims that the breeches had belonged to Saint Francis of Assisi and that she had borrowed them from a nearby monastery to place under the bed as a charm to make her conceive. The husband obligingly returns the garment to the minor friar. (On Jean de Condé, see the note to "The Beaten Path," p. 26.)

Edition: August Scheler, *Dits et Contes de Baudouin de Condé et de Son Fils Jean de Condé.* 3 vols. (Brussels, 1866). II, 121–125.

THE KNIGHT WHO CONJURED VOICES

by Garin

Fabliaux increase, as do their markets,
and fabliards can fill their pockets,
who bring to the idle and roisterous,
wherever the company's not too boisterous,

great easement, and can assuage
all pains, so that even men in a rage
can find in fabliaux relief,
forget their troubles and their grief,
their worries and their enmities.
So says Garin, who never lies,
and who in this story will indite
the adventures of a certain knight
who had a truly remarkable talent,
for he could make cunts speak, this gallant,
and conjure arseholes from all parts
to answer his summons by magic arts.
This gift he got, as you shall hear,
after his dubbing, in the first year
of his knighthood, when though he'd come of age
he still was poor and worked for a wage;
and owning no vineyards and no land,
in tourneys and wars was a hired hand,
for he was handy with a lance and not
a bad fighter in a tight spot,
but gallant and bold when the battle was hot.
Now at this time, as I read the tale,
the spirit of peace begins to prevail:
military ventures fail
to take hold, tourneys are banned,
and men-at-arms are in no demand.
And our knight, having spent the last of his gains,
without a single penny remains.
Gone were his fineries: his gypon,
his ermined tunic, his haubergeon,
his fur-lined cloak, his shirts of lawn;
for he had put them all in pawn.

(I feel he did not show good sense
thus to eat and drink his accouterments.)
So he, with nowhere else to go,
took shelter in a provincial château,
where he had nothing to do from noon till nine
but sample the excellent local wine.
Until one day, when he had spent
long months in idle luxury pent,
came the great news of a tournament,
to be held in Touraine at the town of La Haye,
whither were riding without delay
the greatest and fiercest knights of the day.
Our knight rejoiced, his spirits higher
than ever, and sent for Hugh his squire
to tell him the news; but sober Hugh
said: "What has this to do with you,
who are so far out of your senses
as to pawn your arms to meet expenses?"
"Ah, Hugh!" said the knight, "now I recall
how in spite of your counsel I pawned them all.
If only I'd taken your advice!
But, Hugh, see now if you can devise
some way of getting them out again—
without you I'm the most helpless of men—
quickly, Hugh, and see also whether
you can scrape a little money together."
Hugh, having seen how matters stood,
went about the business as best he could;
and, thinking he must jump if he would fall free,
decided to sell his master's palfrey.
And he bargained so well that he sold the mare
for the worth of the arms and a little to spare.

The following day the knight and Hugh
set forth without a retinue,
and as they were riding through some sedges
the knight asked Hugh how he'd got their pledges.
Hugh, who was wise, looked out at the heath
and said: "Dear master, by my faith,
I sold your palfrey; I could not see
another way for us to get free
of debt, do what I might;
you'll have no horse to lead on your right."
"And how much, Hugh, could you put by?"
"My lord," said Hugh, "to tell no lie,
all we have's twelve measly pence."
"Then we'd better avoid all rash expense,"
said the knight. And, trampling through the heather,
the two of them rode on together.
And when they had traveled a great ways,
they entered a valley. The knight let graze
his horse and rode in thought, but Hugh
set spurs to his nag and onward flew.
Until he happened on a mead
in whose midst a fountain played
of crystal waters pure that poured
in many little streams abroad,
while all around it beautiful trees,
such as only in summer one sees,
all green and leafy, there were planted;
and where the silvery jet decanted
three maidens bathed, so seeming wise
and beautiful, one might surmise
that they were fairies in mortal guise.
Their clothes they'd hung upon a tree,

so rich in stuff and embroidery,
and trimmed in gold and made to pleasure,
they surely were worth a very treasure.
Hugh, when he glimpsed their white charms,
their pretty bosoms, haunches, arms,
spurred horse and did not stop to praise,
but riding by the naked fays,
without so much as a yea or nay,
seized and carried their clothes away.
The nymphs, left standing all aghast
to see the squire ride off so fast,
as if truly he'd no mind to stay,
and their gowns and petticoats carried away,
began to weep and rave and cry out;
and while they thus were flinging about,
up came the knight at a smart pace,
in search of Hugh. The eldest grace
hailed him and told him their plight,
at which, much moved, the worthy knight
set spurs and gave his stallion head,
till he caught Hugh, to whom he said:
"Drop them at once! By my head,
you shall not have them! Nor shall it be said
we acted so basely, in God's name,
as to put those poor naked damsels to shame."
"Calm down," said Hugh. "Consider this thing
from all sides; these clothes will bring
at very least a hundred pounds;
if for fifteen years you made the rounds
of tourneys, jousts, and wars and such,
you could never hope to earn as much."
"By God!" said the knight. "I don't care a jot

what the price is. I'll bring back the lot.
Such booty, won without a fight,
will not increase my worth as a knight."
"Take them," said Hugh in a very sweat
of spite. "You'll deserve what you get!"
The knight snatched up the clothes and rode
at a gallop to where the maids abode.
The three fair damsels were glad to see
him and gladder to have their finery.
They put on their clothes in great haste,
for none of them had a moment to waste,
then took their leave; but the first of the three,
As they were going, said: "God save me,
this is a courteous knight, who to please us
returns us all our gowns and chemises,
which he might have sold for pounds and pence.
To leave him without a recompense
or any cause for gratitude
would be ungenerous and rude.
Let's call him back and pay him well;
the poor man has no wherewithal.
Let none of us be mean, but each
give him enough to make him rich.
The others agreed. They called the knight,
and the eldest fay, as was her right,
spoke first of all and said: "Sir knight,
I swear on my faith, it is not right
that you should ride away like this
after rendering us such services.
For you have saved our lives and can
boast yourself a worthy man.
A rich gift on you I'll bestow:

henceforth, in whatever place you go
all men will greet you and make you brave
welcome and offer you all they have,
so that never again will you be in need."
"Fair dame," said the knight, "for this rich meed
much thanks." The second followed the tall one
and said: "Sir knight, my gift's no small one:
wherever you go, west or east,
you shall not find a maid or a beast,
so she have two eyes, whose cunt can refrain
from answering you if you but deign
to speak to it. There's your reward.
You may be sure no king or lord
has such a gift." The knight grew red
with shame; he thought the girl was mad.
The third one took her turn and said:
"Sir knight, to this second gift I add,
as is just and right, that if the cunt
be blocked or stoppered up in front
and cannot answer you straightway,
the arsehole will, without delay,
speak for it, if you give leave,
no matter whom it hurt or grieve."
Again he blushed—he thought that they
were mocking him—and rode away.
And when he'd caught up again with Hugh,
he told him the tale as I've told it to you:
"The maids of that mead made a fool of me."
"I'm glad to hear it," said Hugh. "By my fay,
that man's a fool who can't keep a grip
on what he has, but lets it slip
or throws it down without a care."

"Hugh," said the knight, "by my head, I swear
you speak the truth." Just then and there
a priest came riding astride a mare.
This priest was rich and well supplied
with gold, but mean and greedy-eyed.
He'd set out alone on the road that day
to go to a town not far away;
but no sooner did he spy the knight
than he reined in his mare and made to alight.
"My lord, you're welcome," he said. "Please stay
and lodge in my house for today.
To honor and serve you is all I crave;
you may command whatever I have,
to the very last thing, of that no fear."
The knight was much amazed to hear
an utter stranger, as was this priest,
invite him home to be his guest.
Then said wise Hugh: "As God has ruth,
my lord, these fays have spoken truth.
That I believe. But try right now
to conjure the cunt of the mare. I vow
it will reply." The knight said: "Agreed,"
and turned at once toward the rump of the steed.
"Sir cunt, where does your master ride?
Now tell me truly and nothing hide."
"By my faith, sir knight," said the cunt, "he's bound
to court his mistress, and girdled round
his middle he carries twenty pound
of good hard coin to buy her a gown."
This priest when he heard the cunt speak so clear,
took to his heels from very fear;
he thought he was betrayed and bewitched.

His cloak from off his shoulders he twitched,
the better to run, and also he pitched
his belt and his money onto the road.
He left his mare where she abode
and turned and ran. The squire Hugh
called after him a loud halloo,
but never a word the priest replied;
he saved his breath to lengthen his stride,
and fled off down a wagon track;
for a hundred pounds he would not have turned back.
The knight picked up the money bag,
while squire Hugh caught hold of the nag,
which was well saddled, and snatched up the cloak;
and laughing heartily at the joke,
they rode off together in great haste.
The knight was very pleased; he placed
the money in squire Hugh's care—
twenty good pounds he carried there.
"Hugh, I'd have had to be drunk," said the knight,
"to leave those honest girls in that plight,
all naked, and steal their gowns for the cloth.
That they were fairies I'll take my oath.
They have given me rich recompense.
It does not matter what great expense
we've had or what we squander or waste;
we've come into plenty from that priest,
who'll pay our bills, though he's ignorant
of this and of how his money is spent.
Hugh, he gains little, it seems to me,
who makes his conquests by knavery;
for, losing his honor, he'll have no report
or fine tales told of him at court.

As for me, I'd rather be blind or lame."
So they rode and chatted, until they came
to a castle, well seated, fair, and strong.
But let me not make my tale too long:
in that castle there dwelt a count,
who more than thirty knights could mount
at his command, and with him his fair
wife, a lady most debonair.
Then straightway this knight who made cunts speak
entered into the castle keep,
where all the people came running to meet him,
they were so eager to welcome and greet him.
This pleased the knight beyond all bounds.
There was a green in the midst of the town,
and all the townsfolk assembled there,
among them the count and his lady fair—
who was no chatterbox or flirt—
and everyone in half hose or skirt:
the burghers and damsels and every knight,
the servants and squires; and at the sight
of our knight, who with Hugh came toward 'em,
from all sides crowded around to board him.
The count himself could not requite
his longing but by hugging him tight,
and kissed him full upon the mouth.
And the countess hugged him; in God's truth,
she'd have kissed him twenty times, full fair,
if the count had not been quite so near,
more willingly than she'd hear a mass.
The knight among the people did pass,
and not a servant or knight-at-arms
but greeted him with open arms.

They led him into the count's hall,
where at once they sat down at table, all
the knights and their peers, for they took no pleasure
in fasting talk. And when at their leisure
they'd dined, began to talk of sleep,
for the night was very dark and deep.
The countess took great pains to please
her guest, and so he might be at his ease,
made a rich bed in a lovely chamber,
where all alone he could rest and slumber.
And when she had done this, she called a maid,
the prettiest of her damsels, and said
to her secretly: "Go, sweet friend,
and lie with that knight whom the heavens send
to please us all. Go freely and bide,
all naked, as long as you like, by his side.
It cannot grieve you, for the knight is fair.
I'd go there myself, nor would I care
a straw for shame, were it not that I dread
the count my lord, who is still not abed."
"Willingly, lady," said the maid,
"will I serve you in this." For she was afraid
to refuse and also eager to try.
She entered the room where the knight did lie,
all atremble, and there as best she might
she took off her clothes and lay down by the knight.
The knight, when he felt her by his side,
woke up at once, surprised, and cried:
"Who is it now that lies with me?"
"My lord, don't take it ill," said she,
who was a simple maid and coy.
"I do not mean to harm or annoy.

I'm a maid in the countess's employ;
she sent me here, of that no dread.
I only want to caress your head."
"In faith, that doesn't displease me a bit,"
he said, and by way of proving it
he embraced her and kissed her mouth and cheek
and felt her breasts that were pretty and sleek.
Then to touch her cunt the knight made free
and said: "Sir cunt, now speak to me!
I would know how your mistress came by my side."
"My lord," said the cunt, "there's nothing I'd hide;
the countess sent the maid in her stead
to bring you pleasure and joy abed."
When the maiden heard her cunt speak out,
she was shaken strangely by terror and doubt;
she started up and leapt out of bed,
all naked but for her shirt, and fled.
She ran into her mistress's chamber,
and the heart within her beat like a tambour.
The countess called her and said: "What news?
What's happened to you? Did you refuse
the knight to whom I sent you?" The maid,
as best she could, found voice and said:
"My lady, I've never been so daunted;
I think that man in there's enchanted.
I went to him and took off my gown
and all naked by his side lay down;
but no sooner was I in bed, to speak blunt,
than he took to calling on my cunt;
and in my hearing my cunt complied
and to everything he asked replied."
The countess gaped at what she heard

but said she didn't believe a word
of such marvels; at which the maiden swore
that she'd told the truth and nothing more.
There they left the tale without further gloze.
The next morning early the knight arose
and called to Hugh to saddle his horse.
The countess broke her usual course,
when she heard the knight was going away,
and got up early to bid him stay,
and begged him at very least to delay
till he'd had dinner. The knight replied:
"Lady, God save me, I would not bide,
for all the world, until dinnertime.
Let it not displease you, I must decline,
for I've a very long journey ahead."
"No matter for that," the countess said,
"You'll make your journey another day."
And the knight, who saw that there was no way
for him to refuse, consented to stay.
And when after dinner the knights at table
began to parley, the countess, unable
to hold her tongue, spoke loud in the hall
and said: "My lords, so may God save us all,
I have heard many knights and squires tell
their adventures, and servants and burghers as well,
but none of them can boast and say
they've done what I heard yesterday.
For know, in this castle there is a knight
who all the world surpasses in might;
so puissant he that at his whim
he can conjure cunts to speak to him.
High praise a man like that may claim!

And, by Saint German, he is this same
knight, our guest who yesterday came."
When the knights had heard her, they much admired
this marvel, and of the knight inquired
if that was true which the lady gave out.
"Yes," said the knight, "without any doubt."
At this the count and all his men
laughed out loud. Then spoke once again
the dame, who was neither foolish nor base,
and said: "Sir knight, whatever the case,
I'll bet you forty pounds my cunt
will never be so mad or so drunk
as to speak to you a single word."
As soon as the knight this challenge heard,
he said: "My lady, so God me save,
forty pounds I do not have,
but my horse and armor, for what they'll fetch,
I'll bet here and now, if you'll stake as much."
"I don't ask better than that," said the dame,
"and you'll get forty pounds just the same,
if you win, but if you lose, now mind,
you leave on foot and your gear stays behind."
The knight agreed, and to be precise
as to what must happen, in which he was wise,
he said: "My lady, the cunt will pronounce
at least three consecutive words at once."
"If you wish," she said, "take seven or eight.
But before you do, I'll ask you to wait
while I go to my room for a bit." She heard
no demur or contradictory word;
the bet was clinched, and the countess went in
to her chamber. Now hear how she planned to win:

She filled her fist with a good lump
of cotton and stuffed it up her cunt;
the countess calked her seam aright
and with her right fist rammed it tight;
more than a pound of it she inducted,
so that the cunt was well obstructed.
And when she had shoved enough cotton in
to fill it up to the very brim,
she returned to the hall and challenged the knight
to do his worst, for do what he might,
her organ to gossip was never wont,
it would not give him a word or a grunt.
The knight answered nothing but called on the cunt:
"Sir cunt, I call on you to remember
what your lady did in her chamber
when she retired, and tell me why."
But the cunt was unable to reply—
so stuffed with cotton was its throat
that it could not utter a single note.
The knight put the question to it again,
but it wouldn't as much as say amen,
for it was mute. The knight in great ire
turned to ask advice of his squire,
and gave up as lost both horse and gear.
"My lord," Hugh answered, "have no fear!
Remember now what the third maid said:
if the cunt were silent, the arsehole instead
would speak. I'm sure she told no lie."
"Hugh," laughed the knight, "as I live and must die,
you speak the truth!" To the arsehole now
he turned and politely asked it how
it was the cunt no answer would grant.

The arsehole said: "Because he can't;
for both his mouth and throat are full,
I'm not sure whether of cotton or wool.
It was my lady stuffed him so
when she went to her room a moment ago.
But if the cotton were out, why then
I'm sure that he would speak again."
When the knight had heard the arsehole's account,
at once he spoke to his host the count
and said: "My lord, by the faith I owe,
the countess has done me wrong to go
and stopple up her cunt; for know,
it would speak if she hadn't crammed it so."
Then the count gave the order immediately
that the countess set her organ free.
The countess returned to her room, where she,
who knew that the count no refusal would brook,
pulled out all the cotton by means of a hook;
she repented that she had stuffed it at all.
Then back she went into the hall;
she knew full well the wager was lost,
a foolish bet which she'd made to her cost.
The knight called the cunt and asked it why
at his first call it would not reply.
Said the cunt: "I could not, I was so choked
with the cotton my mistress had crammed down my throat."
The count laughed loud, and all his men
laughed at the joke again and again,
and told the countess she'd lost; it were best
she say no more, but make peace with her guest.
This she did, and also, without delay,
the forty pounds to the knight did pay.

And he received with joy what he won, he
stood in such great need of money;
and as long as he lived he was honored by all.
Now wasn't he born in good hour to fall
into such good fortune the very year
he was dubbed! My story ends here.

"Le Chevalier Qui Fist Parler les Cons" is preserved in no less than
seven manuscripts, a clear testimony to its popularity in the Middle
Ages. The tale, which may well have inspired *Les Bijoux Indiscrets*
("The Telltale Jewels") of Diderot, offers overtones of parody of
chivalric literature in the opposition between the idealistic knight and
the worldly-wise but unscrupulous squire, Hugh, who are not unlike
the knight and squire of the most famous of all parodies of chivalric
ideals, Cervantes' *Don Quixote*. The story of our fabliau was retold at
least once in German literature, in "Der Weisse Rosendorn" ("The
White Rosebush"), included in Von der Hagen's *Gesammtabenteuer*
(*Collected Tales,* 1850).

Nothing is known about the Garin who, in line 10, claims to be the
author as well as the reciter of this tale. The dialect of the work is
probably that of the Parisian area of the mid-thirteenth century. Also,
the author may have been associated with the city mentioned in
the work, La Haye, although this name might have been chosen only
for the sake of the rhyme.

Edition: Rychner, II, 38–79 (version C).

THE PARTRIDGES

Since I am accustomed to telling fabliaux, I should like now, instead of a fable, to tell a true story about a peasant who by chance caught two partridges alongside his hedge. He took great care with their preparation and ordered his wife to put them on the fire. She knew well how to go about it. And while she was making the fire and getting the spit ready the peasant ran quickly to fetch the priest. But he was so long in returning that the partridges were cooked before he got back.

The wife set the spit and took a pinch of the skin, for she was very much given to gluttony whenever God provided something to eat. She did not seek after great wealth, but only to fulfill all her little desires. She rushed to attack the first partridge and ate both its wings. Then she went into the street to see if her husband was coming. When she saw that he wasn't, she came back into the house and treated the rest of the bird in the same way. Woe to the piece which was left!

Then she began to think that she might eat the other partridge as well. She knew very well what she would say if she was asked what had become of them. She would say that while she was putting them away the cats came and snatched them out of her hands, each one carrying off a partridge. So she would escape the blame. Then she went to stand in the street to watch for her husband. When she saw that he wasn't coming, her mouth began to water for the partridge that was left. She would go mad if she didn't have just a little piece of it. She pulled off the neck very gently and ate it with great gusto, licking her fingers all over. "Alas!" she said. "What shall I do? If I eat it all, what shall I say? But how can I keep from eating it? I have such a great desire for it! Now come what may, I must eat it all!"

The peasant was away long enough for his wife to eat her fill, and immediately after he returned. He came into the house and cried out: "Hey there! Are the partridges cooked?" "Husband," the wife said, "things have taken a bad turn. The cat has eaten them." At once the peasant leaped up and ran at her like a madman. He would have torn her eyes out then and there if she had not cried: "It's a joke! It's a joke! Get out, Sathanas! I've covered them to keep them warm." "It's a good thing," said he, "or, by the faith I owe Saint Martin, I would have sung you a dirty tune. Now I'll take my good wooden tankard and my best white table-cloth and spread them under my cloak beneath the bower in the meadow." "But take your knife too," said the wife, "which badly needs sharpening, and sharpen it a little on the stone in the courtyard."

The peasant took off his coat and ran about his business, the naked blade in his hand. Just then up came the priest, who arrived to get his share of the partridges. He went straight to the lady and embraced her tenderly. But she said to him softly: "Fly! Fly! I will not be present to see you put to shame and your body mutilated. My husband has gone out to sharpen his best knife, and he says he intends to castrate you if he can catch you."

"As you are mindful of God," said the priest, "what are you saying? We were to eat two partridges which your husband caught just this morning." "By Saint Martin," said the wife, "there is no partridge here nor any other bird. I would be pleased to give you something to eat, but I would be grieved by your suffering. But look there how he is sharpening his knife!" "I see him," said the priest. "On my word, I believe you spoke the truth." He didn't extend his visit, but ran off with great speed. And the wife called out joyfully: "My lord Gombaut, come here!" "What's wrong?" said her husband. "What's wrong?" she said. "You'll find out soon enough. But if you don't run at once, you'll be the loser, I think. For by the faith I owe you, the priest has carried off your partridges."

The good man became furious. With the knife in his hand, he ran after the priest. And when he caught sight of him he yelled: "You won't get away with them like that!" Then at the top of his lungs he shouted: "You're carrying them all hot, but you'll leave them here if I catch you! You won't be much of a friend if you eat them without me." The priest looked behind him and saw the peasant pursuing. When he saw the knife in his hand, he thought he was a dead man if he was caught. He didn't just play at running. And the peasant pressed on, thinking to recover the partridges, but the priest in a great burst gained his house and locked himself in.

The peasant returned home and questioned his wife. "By God!" he said, "now tell me how you lost the partridges." And his wife said: "As God may save me! as soon as the priest saw me, he begged me, as I loved him, to show him the partridges, because he was very eager to see them. I brought him straight to where I had put them, and he reached out his hands, seized them, and ran away. But rather than follow him I let you know at once." Her husband replied: "You may well be speaking the truth. But let's let him be for now."

So was the priest tricked, and Gombaut also who caught the partridges. I have told this tale as a lesson to show that woman was made to deceive. She turns lies into truth and truth into lies. He who wrote this fabliau and these words does not wish to spin them out any longer.

Presumably from the pen of a Goliard poet, the anonymous fabliau "Les Perdriz" is a subtle and humorously conceived tale which turns about a double misunderstanding. Several familiar ingredients of the fabliau—the naïve peasant, his sensual wife, and the lecherous priest —are combined in a swiftly moving and humorous triangle tale. The plot hinges on the fact, slyly alluded to, that the priest has visited the house also in the husband's absence. The priest's narrow escape from castration recalls another fabliau of this collection, "The Poor Student."

The plot of "The Partridges" is one of those widely current in folk traditions down to the present day. Folktale versions have been collected as far away as Ceylon and southern India; in France the tale has been recorded from Brittany, Lorraine, and Gascony. Written analogues are also very numerous: versions, probably deriving directly or indirectly from the fabliau, have been retold in medieval German, notably in "Der Entlaufene Hasenbraten" ("The Escaped Hare") from the *Gesammtabenteuer* (1850), and in the tale "Das Gluge Gretel" ("Clever Gretel") from *Grimm's Fairy Tales*. The story was reworked many times in French; for instance, in *Les Contes aux Heures Perdues* (*Tales for Leisure Hours;* 1643) of Antoine le Métel, Sieur d'Ouville, as well as in Italian and Spanish.

Edition: Karl Bartsch, *Chrestomathie de l'Ancien Français* (Leipzig, 1927), pp. 200–201.

THE POOR STUDENT

I do not wish to make a long tale. This fabliau tells us the story of a student who lived in Paris until his poverty forced him to leave that city. He had nothing left to pawn or sell, and he saw clearly that he could no longer remain there where life was so hard. And since he had no means of livelihood, he thought it would be better to leave his studies and take the road to his own country. This he did, journeying like one who is very eager to get where he is going. But he had not the least bit of money with him and so was in great distress.

The day he started out he neither drank nor ate until he came to a town, where he entered the house of a peasant. There was no one home but a servant and the wife, who the student thought was very proud in manner. He asked her to give him lodging for love and charity's sake. "Sir student," she said, "my husband is not at home just now, and I believe he would find fault with me if I lodged you or anyone else without his leave." To this the student replied: "Lady, I come from school, and I have been journeying a great while today. Now act like a courteous woman and give me lodging without further talk." The lady made further excuses, more than she had found at first. Meanwhile a lad came up with two pots of wine, which the wife took and put away as quick as she could. The servant was preparing a pancake, and she took some pork out of the pot and put it on a platter. "Really, lady," said the student, "I should be very pleased to stay with you." At which she said quite bluntly: "Sir student, I don't wish to give you lodging. Go look elsewhere." So the student went away, and the wife, who was in a hurry, shut the door on his heels.

But he had gone only a little way when he met a priest, all wrapped up in his black hood, who passed right by him without saying a word and entered the house which the student had left.

While the student was wondering aloud in what place he might find lodging, a good man heard him complain and at once began to question him: "Who are you who passes there?" "Indeed, I am a very weary student, for I have not ceased traveling today, and I still cannot find lodging." "By God and by Saint Nicholas, sir student, don't be distressed, for you have found a lodging. Tell me, have you been to that house over there?" "Lord," said the student, "I have just now left it." "Now go back boldly, for by the faith I owe Saint Clement, the house is mine, and I will make it ready for you or for anyone I wish. I have come directly from the mill, and I am bearing wheaten flour to make bread for my children."

Then hand in hand the two of them went straight to the door; and the good man, with his burden on him, began to knock and call out loudly. At once the priest heard him, and the wife said: "Ah, sir priest, for love's sake hurry, quickly, and hide in that cupboard. And be easy, for I will make him go to bed as soon as I can." And the priest, without delay, threw himself into the cupboard.

The good man called until she opened the door for him, and he and the student came in. "Now, sir student," said the lord of the house, "take off your cloak and be joyful and merry, for if you are I will be too. Wife, what are you doing? Aren't you going to prepare something for us to eat?" "My lord," she said, "forgive me but I have nothing to prepare for you." Then the lord began to swear: "By the saints of God! are you telling the truth?" "Indeed," said his wife, "you know very well what you left here when you went to the mill this morning." "Wife," said he, "God bless me, I wasn't thinking at all. It's just that I'm so sorry for this student." "My lord," she said, "you must do the best you can now. A meal is quickly prepared." Then she turned to the servant and said: "Take the flour and go make them some bread to eat. Then let them go to bed."

The lord of the house was very much distressed, but he turned to the student and said: "Sir student, as God may save me, you must have heard many things, so tell us a tale now or a song or a story from a book while we are waiting for them to cook our meal for this evening." The student answered him briefly: "My lord, I can't tell a fable because I don't know any, but I will tell you willingly about a fearful adventure I had. I know nothing about fabliaux, but I shall tell you about my scare." "You shall be quit of your obligation," said the lord, "if you tell us about your fright. For I know that you are not by nature a maker of fabliaux. But now, for love's sake, tell us your story."

"Sir," said the student, "briefly this is it: Today I went by a wood, and when I had passed through it, I came upon a great herd of pigs, large and small, black and yellow. There were many fat pigs, but the herdsman was not there. And as I was looking at the pigs a huge wolf came along and carried off one of them with great speed. It was certainly a very fat pig; his flesh was as fat as the pork the maid took out of the pot a short time ago."

As soon as the lady heard this, she gave up all hope. "What is this, wife?" said the good man. "Does the student tell the truth?" She knew that a denial wouldn't be worth a farthing. "Yes, sir," she said, "without a doubt I did go and buy some." "Lady," said the good man, "that makes me happy, for now there is proper food. Now, sir student, go on with your tale, for tonight we are without cares."

The student did not hang back from telling his story: "Sir, when I saw how the wolf seized the pig, I was much afflicted. The wolf was not slow to eat it; he tore it to pieces thus. I watched for a long while how the blood dripped from it; it was just as red as the wine which the boy brought to this house this evening when I asked for lodging."

The wife was so angry she didn't know what to say. Then the husband said to her: "What is this, wife? Do we have wine?" "Yes, husband, by Saint Martin, we have a great quantity of it. Certainly I had you in mind much more than I said." "Wife," he said, "may God look at me! Think of that! This makes me very happy. And I am happier still for the sake of this student whom we are sheltering. Sir student, go on with your tale."

"Indeed, sir," said the student, "willingly. The wolf was very fierce, and I didn't know what to do. But I looked about to see if I could find something to strike him with. I don't know what else to tell you: I found a wide stone; I think it would be no lie to say that the cake which the servant made a while ago and which is in there is much wider than the stone was."

The lady knew and heard, and she saw that it was no use trying to conceal the matter. The husband looked at her and said: "What's this, wife? Do we have cake?" "Yes, indeed," said the wife, "and a fine lovely one, all made of eggs." "Then our trial is over, thank God!" said the husband. "In faith, sir student, that scare of yours was a lucky thing. Now you can enjoy a good meal, for we have bread and wine and meat. I have only you to thank for this. Now, is the story of your fright all over?"

"Not yet, may God bless me, it won't end like that. For when I had picked up the stone, I thought to throw it at the wolf, and he turned and looked at me just as the priest is looking at me now out of the window of that cupboard over there."

"Priest!" the husband exclaimed. "Is there then a priest in here?" Then he could not contain himself, but jumped to his feet and ran at once to seize hold of the priest. The priest tried to defend himself, but he struggled in vain, for the good man caught him at once. He stripped him of his habit, and he gave his cloak and his hood to the student who had told the story of the fearful adventure. Indeed, he gave that priest what he deserved and put him to great shame.

This fabliau is an exemplum of that peasant proverb: "One

should not deny bread to anyone, not even to him whom one never expects to see again." For one can never know what things may come, even the most common. Many people have suffered this way, but this wife most of all, who was so inhospitable to the student when he asked her for lodging. For he would not have said a word of what he told that night if she had but given him what he asked for.

The anonymous fabliau "Le Povre Clerc" is the story of the unwelcome guest who, while pretending to relate a tale, reveals to the husband the iniquities of his wife. In the terms of the folklorist it belongs to the class of themes called *retorts from hungry persons*. The tale is typical of the fabliau spirit. The characters are stock, save perhaps for that of the peasant, who is viewed with an unusual benevolence. The contrast between the warm, lush interior, with its emphasis on food and comfort, and the plight of the destitute student is artistically drawn.

The story is one of those which has wide currency in narrative literature, with versions extant from Japan and India to the West. In Italian it is found in the *Pentamerone* (ii, 10) of Basile (1575–1632) and in the tale "De Vana Luxuria" ("Vain Concupiscence") of Giovanni Sercambi (1347–1424). In German the fabliau is retold in the *Gesammtabenteuer* (1850), No. III, 61, where it is called "Der Geäffte Pfaffe" ("The Duped Priest"), and as "Von Einem Varnden Schuler" ("The Travelling Student") from a *Fastnachtspiele* (Shrovetide play). It is preserved also in *Les Contes aux Heures Perdues* (*Tales for Leisure Hours; 1643*) of Antoine le Métel, Sieur d'Ouville, and it was finally reworked in French verse by Barthélemy Imbert in the eighteenth century. The last element of the fabliau, in which the wife's clerical paramour is forced unexpectedly to hide in the cupboard while another eats his food, recalls a second fabliau, "Le Clerc Qui Fu Repus Derriere l'Escrin" ("The Cleric Hidden Behind the Screen"), by Jean de Condé.

Edition: Montaiglon-Raynaud, V, 192–200.

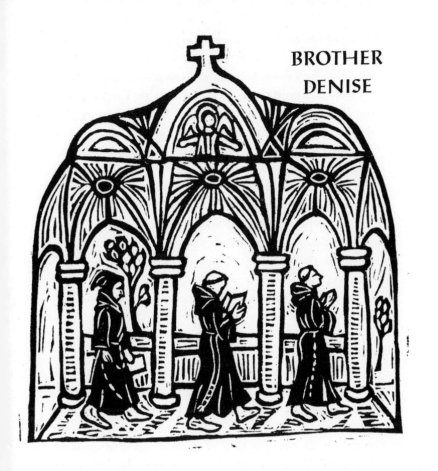

BROTHER DENISE

by Rutebeuf

The habit does not make the monk. If a man dwells in a hermitage and wears the clothes that belong to it, I don't care two straws for clothes and habit if he does not lead as pure a life as his clothes would indicate. But many people make a brave show and a great pretense to worth who are like those trees which bear no fruit but are very beautiful in bloom. Such folk well deserve to live in great misery and shame. As the proverb says, all that glitters is not gold.

That is why I must, before I die, compose a tale about the most beautiful creature to be found between Paris and England. I'll tell you how it happened: More than twenty great noblemen sought her hand, but in no manner did she wish to enter into matrimony. Rather, she had consecrated her virginity to God and to Our Lady. This maiden was a gentlewoman; her father had been a knight. She had a mother but no sister or brother, and it seems that the maiden and her mother were deeply attached to each other.

Certain Franciscan brothers, passing through that region, frequented their house, and one of them, who hung about there, cast a spell on the young girl. I'll tell you how he did it. The maiden begged him to ask her mother to let her join a religious order. And he said to her: "My dear child, if you wish to lead the life which Saint Francis has prescribed, as do we, I see no reason why you should fail to become a saint." The girl, who in a moment was touched, persuaded, convinced, and conquered, as soon as she heard the Franciscan's words, exclaimed: "As God may honor me, there is nothing I should take greater joy in than to be allowed to join your order. In a happy hour God gave me life if I can take my vows there." When the brother heard what she said, he replied: "Sweet maiden, as God may love me, if I could be sure that you wished to enter our order and that you could, without deception, preserve your virginity, know that in truth I would have you inducted into our order."

The maiden promised him that she would keep her maidenhead all the days of her life. Then this friar took her in and deceived her who suspected no guile. On her soul he forbade her to reveal anything he had told her and said that secretly, so that nobody should know, he would have her beautiful blond hair cut and her head tonsured; and he would have her dress in man's clothes, and in that disguise she would go straight to the place where he was in authority. Then he, who was falser than Herod, set a date to meet her and took his leave.

She wept many tears when she saw him go, he who was to make her take in the appendix of his text and put her in a false position—may the plague take him and finish him off! She thought everything he preached was prophecy, and she gave her heart to God. He made a gift of his heart too, a gift for which God would give him a just reward. For his thoughts were very different from those good thoughts which passed through her head; they were entirely at odds, for she thought to make a retreat and withdraw from the pride of this world, while he, in whom sin abounded, was all burning with the fires of lust and had set his thoughts on bringing the maiden to that hot bath in which, please God, he wished to steep himself and where she would never refuse him or deny him anything he asked.

The brother went along thinking these thoughts; and his companion, who was walking with him, surprised that he did not speak, said to him: "What are you thinking about, Brother Simon?" "I am thinking about a sermon," said he, "the best one I ever devised." "Then go on thinking," said the other. Brother Simon could not defend his heart or keep it from dwelling on the maiden; and she longed for the moment when her waist would be girded with the cord of the Franciscans. She rehearsed in her heart the lesson which the friar had given her. Within three days she had slipped away from the mother who bore her. The mother was very much distressed, for she did not know what had become of her daughter, and, weeping, she mourned for her every day of the week.

But the daughter didn't care about that and thought only of going away. She had her beautiful locks clipped like a boy's and put on man's clothes and breeches (her face really resembled a young man's), and in that guise she came to the rendezvous which the friar had appointed. The friar, whom the Adversary urged, incited, and egged on, was overjoyed at her coming. He had her received into the order (he well knew how to deceive his brothers), gave her the habit of the order, had a great tonsure made on her head, and brought her into the church of the monastery. She knew quite well how to behave, both in the cloister and in the church; she knew her whole psalter by heart and was very good at chanting the office. Very beautifully and elegantly she sang with the others in church and behaved very correctly in all things. So Mistress Denise (the brothers never changed her name, but called her Brother Denise) had everything her heart desired.

Now what shall I tell you more? This Brother Simon got along so well with her that at last he opened his heart to her and taught her certain new games, and that in such a way that no one noticed it. By her behavior she deceived all her brothers. She was courteous and serviceable, and every brother in the monastery was very fond of Brother Denise. And fonder still was Brother Simon. He often hitched himself to the shaft, and, like a good shaft horse, could hardly be dragged from it; he liked that better than plainsong. He taught her her paternoster and she very willingly absorbed it. So he led the life of a lecher and forsook the life of an apostle.

He led her everywhere through the country—he wanted no other companion—until one day, by chance, they came to the house of a knight who had good wines in his cellar and who was willing to share some with them. The lady gazed long at Brother Denise, taking note of her face and bearing, and she saw that Brother Denise was a woman. She wanted to make sure of that, so when the table was removed she, being a quick-witted woman, took Brother Denise by the hand and, smiling at her husband, she said: "Fair lord, go outside there and amuse yourself, and let us make two parties of us four. Do you go with Brother Simon, and Brother Denise will remain to hear my confession." This did not please the two companions at all. The Franciscan would rather have been at Pontoise. They were both distressed at the lady's proposal, for they were afraid of being found out. Brother Simon went up to the lady and said to her: "Lady, I will hear your confession, for this brother has no license to give you absolution." And she answered: "Fair sir, I wish to tell my sins to him and speak to him about confession."

Then she brought Brother Denise into her room, where she closed the door and locked it securely. And, when Brother Denise was shut up with her, she said: "Sweet friend, who gave you such foolish advice to join this order? So may God grant me remission of my sins when my soul leaves my body, you will be nothing the worse for telling me the truth. I swear by the Holy Ghost you may confide in me." Brother Denise was very much frightened, and tried as best she could to get out of it. But the lady brought her around by arguments against which she had no defense. Then on her knees

[139]

Brother Denise begged her indulgence and with joined hands besought her not to put her to shame. She told her everything, from beginning to end: how Brother Simon had enticed her away from her mother's home and who she was; she concealed nothing from her.

Then the lady called the friar, and in her husband's presence she put him to greater shame by what she said than any man has ever suffered. "Deceitful bigot! false hypocrite! you lead a false and filthy life. If someone would hang you with that cord of yours, which has so many knots in it, he would do a good day's work. It's people like you, who look good outside but are all rotten within, who bring the world to ruin. The nurse who gave you suck brought up an evil nursling, you who have brought this beautiful creature to such shame. Such an order, by Saint Denis, is neither gentle nor worthy nor honest. You forbid good people dances and balls, fiddles, drums, zithers, and the pleasures of minstrelsy; well now, tell me, Sir Shavetop, did Saint Francis lead the kind of life you lead? You well deserve to be put to shame as a false and proven traitor, and you have happened on someone who will see to it you get what's coming to you." Then she opened a great coffer and made as if to put him into it. The friar threw himself flat on his face before the lady with his arms outstretched as on a cross.

The knight, who was generous and had a soft heart, when he saw the friar in the attitude of crucifixion, took pity on him and raised him up with his right hand. "Brother," he said, "do you want to get free of this business? Then go find at least a hundred pounds to make a dowry for this damsel." When the friar heard these words, he was happier than he'd ever been in all his life. He gave his word that he would bring the money to the knight; he had a good notion as to how to get it without putting anything in pawn. Then he took his leave and went away.

The lady very generously kept Mistress Denise with her. She did not seek to frighten her in any way, but prayed her earnestly to be quite certain that no creature would ever know her secret or that she had been to bed with a man, so nothing would stand in the way of her marrying. Let her choose among the men of her country the one she wanted most, if he were of her rank. The lady, by her kindness, restored Denise to a good frame of mind; nor did she tease her about anything. She brought one of her most beautiful dresses to her bedside, and in all sincerity she comforted her as best she could. "My sweet friend," she said, "you may wear this dress tomorrow." And with her own hand she drew her night-clothes on when she went to bed. She let no one else touch her, for being a wise and courteous lady, she wished to carry out her plan secretly and discreetly.

Quietly she sent for Denise's mother; and that lady had great joy in her heart when she saw the daughter whom she thought she had lost. The lady made the mother believe that her daughter had been in the convent of the Daughters of God and that the lady had taken her from a nun who brought her to the castle because she was in danger of losing her mind.

But why should I repeat all the words they said to one another? Such chatter is worth nothing. Let me say only that Denise remained at the castle until the money was brought. After that she hardly waited a moment before she was betrothed, as she herself chose, to a knight who had asked for her hand some time ago. Then was she called Lady Denise, and she enjoyed considerably more honor than she had had in the habit of a Franciscan.

The fabliau entitled "Frère Denise," composed by the well-known thirteenth-century poet Rutebeuf, is a pointed satire on the mendicant orders, especially the Franciscans, at a time of tension between the latter and the faculty of the University of Paris, a subject which Rutebeuf was to exploit in numerous other poems. The work itself is not a story with a tightly constructed plot like those of the majority of the fabliaux, but the account of a grossly hypocritical deception which has a happy outcome. Rutebeuf is at his satirical best in the humor, superbly cynical and reminiscent of Rabelais, of his indictment of members of a religious order which enjoyed the reputation of lapsing a little too often from virtue.

The specifically Christian context of the story excludes its occurrence in other than Western cultures, but in Europe the theme was widely exploited. The idea of a girl entering a monastery seems to be original with Rutebeuf, though it may have been suggested by an actual event. A sixteenth-century chronicle relates that in 1577 this situation was discovered in a monastery in Paris, the lady's name being Brother Anthony. After Rutebeuf's time many related tales are found: in German, the "Von Keuschen Mönchen Historia" ("The Story of the Chaste Monk") from Hans Wilhelm Kirchhof's *Wendunmuth* (1563); in Italy, there are analogous stories in novella form in the collection of Malespini and in Straparola's *Le Piacevoli Notti* (*Nights of Pleasantries;* 1550). But it was in France that Rutebeuf's fabliau was most imitated. It is found as No. 60 in the *Cent Nouvelles Nouvelles* (*Hundred New Tales;* 1461), and as Tale 31 of Marguerite de Navarre's *Heptameron* (1558), and it passed through Henri Etienne's *Apologie pour Hérodote* (*Apology for Herodotus;* 1566), before arriving at La Fontaine, who included it in his *Contes* (*Tales*) as "Les Cordeliers de Catalogne" ("The Franciscans of Catalonia"). A close parallel in spirit, if not in actual situation, is the tenth tale of the third day from Boccaccio's *Decameron,* which relates a particularly licentious tale of a hermit who, pretending "to put the devil back into hell," seduced a naïve young girl and lived with her in his desert hermitage until he grew weary of her.

The author of the fabliau, Rutebeuf, is usually considered the prototype of the jongleur of medieval literature. Nothing is known about his life or personality except what his work reveals. He was a native of the east of France, probably the city of Troyes in Champagne, where he composed his earliest-known work in 1249. Perhaps as early as 1252 he had migrated to Paris, where in 1254 he wrote his first work concerned with the university controversies, *La Discorde de l'Université et des Jacobins* (*The Discord Between the University and the Jacobins*). He died sometime after 1277, the date of the last work unmistakably from his pen. Rutebeuf, like Jean Bodel, was a prolific writer. Many of his poems have survived, on subjects ranging from the Church, the religious orders, and the University of Paris to the Crusades. He also left us a series of poems in a personal vein, describing the wretchedness of his life in Paris, lives of several well-known saints, and a group of humorously ribald works, among which are five fabliaux.

Edition: Edmond Faral and Julia Bastin, *Œuvres Complètes de Rutebeuf.* 2 vols. (Paris, 1960). II, 283–291.

THE WIDOW

by Gautier le Leu

My lords, I should like to instruct you. We all of us must go off to the wars, on that expedition from which no man returns. And do you know how they dispose of someone who has been convoked to that army? They carry him to the church on a litter, toes up and with great speed; and his wife follows after him. Those who are closest to the wife lay hands and arms on her to keep her from, at the very least, beating her palms together. For she cries out in a loud voice: "Holy Mother Mary, fair lady! It is a wonder I can keep going, I am so full of grief and affliction! I have more pain than I can bear! How grieved I am that I live on! How hard and bitter is this life! May it not be God's will that I travel much farther on this road, but let me be laid with my husband, to whom I swore my faith!"

So she carries on, acting her part, in which there is scarcely a word of truth. At the entrance of the church she begins again her business of shrieking and wailing. The priest, who would like to get on with the collection, quickly orders the candles to be lit; and when he has asked God's pardon for the dead man, he says the mass in a great hurry. When the service is finished and the corpse has been laid on his back in the black earth among the worms, then the good wife wants to jump into the open grave. Whoever should see her then, trembling and blinking her eyes open and shut and beating her fists together, would say: "That woman could very well lose her mind." And so they pull her back, and two of them hold her from behind and bring her all the way home. There her neighbors make her drink cold water to cool off her grief.

At the door of her house she begins all over again: "My husband, what has become of you? You have not come back to me. My God, why have you been taken from me? When I think how your wealth had increased, how your business prospered, how well everything was going for you! How well your workaday clothes fit you and how becoming was your Sunday suit, which we had made on New Year's Day! Oh, Magpie, you told me the truth! And you, Heron, how I cursed you for squawking so much this year! You, Dog, how often you howled! And you, Chicken, you sang me a warning! Oh, Devil, how have you bewitched me so that I cannot conjure my love in God's name to return to me! If it were possible to raise a dead man, I would pay any tribute to do so. God, how I dreamed this year—although I have said nothing about it—base, shameful dreams! May God turn them to my advantage! Husband, the day before yesterday I dreamt that you were in the church, and both the doors were locked. And now you are locked in the earth! And then, immediately after that, I dreamt that you had a black cloak and a pair of great leaden boots, and dressed so you dived into the water and never came up again. You died only a short time after. Those dreams really came true.

"I dreamt that you were dressed in a coat with a great hood. In your hands you held a stone with which you beat down the wall of the house. Lord, what a hole you left me there! No one mourned for you, but I do so again and again! Then it seemed to me—but I am very loth to speak of it—that in my dream a dove, white and beautiful, descended into my breast and made the wall whole again. I do not know what this last dream means."

Then begin the buzzings, the counsels, the parliaments of relatives and neighbors, of nieces and cousins: "In all charity, my good lady, you must find a good man, someone who is neither a fool nor a rascal, to take over this property and maintain this house." Upon which the wife may be seen to make a sad face and answer sharply: "Ladies, I have no inclination that way. Henceforth may God curse those who make such proposals to me, for they do not please me at all." Then she curses all her pretty clothes.

So let us leave the lady to tell over her sorrows and misfortunes, and speak of her husband, who in all his life had never contented her. He is led to the great judgment seat up above, where he will be given short shrift if he cannot account for all his actions here below, and he is held accountable for the smallest things. He cries out and calls on his household, for whom he has provided so well, and on his relatives and friends, on whom he has bestowed his wealth, to come and help him, for the love of God. But this is something that no man may hope for. Then with a sad face he calls on his wife, who was so dear to him; but that lady has other concerns. A sweet sensation pricks her heart and lifts up her spirit, and arouses in the bearded counselor under her skirts an appetite for meat, neither peacock nor crane, but that dangling sausage for which so many are eager.

The lady is no longer concerned with the dead; so she washes herself and dresses up and dyes her frock yellow and tucks up her furbelows and does over her jabots, her ruffles, and her lace cuffs. She puts on her best things, and as a new-molted falcon goes flapping through the air, so does the lady go sporting and showing herself off from street to street. She greets people with great ingenuousness, bowing right down to the ground. Repeatedly she closes her mouth tight and purses her lips. She is neither lazy nor bitter nor sour nor quarrelsome, but sweeter than cinnamon, quicker turning and more agile than a tambourine or a weather vane. Her heart flies on wings. She is not inclined to grow angry or to complain or to scold, but rather seeks to appear both good and full of humility. And she often pulls her wimple forward to hide her hollow cheeks, which look like open eggshells.

And now that I have told you of her manner and in what style she was dressed, let me say briefly what sort of life she leads, both on Sundays and weekdays. On Monday she sets out on her way; and whoever she meets, be she blond or brunette, she lets her understand what is on her mind. So she comes and goes the entire day. She has many things to remember and when she goes to bed at night, then does she begin to make her rounds. Her heart opens wide, and she sends it forth to the many places where people have hardly any use for her. No night is so dark as to keep her heart from

voyaging. Then she says over and over again: "It's my opinion that I would suit this one well; he is a fine young man.
But that one wouldn't be interested in me at all if my friends
should bring up the subject. And there is nothing for me
in that other one; he's not worth two eggs." So she goes on
all night, for there is no one to keep her from it. And, when
morning comes, she says to herself: "I was born lucky! For
there is no one who can order me about. I need fear nobody,
neither friend nor stranger, neither brown nor blond nor
redheaded. My halter is broken." She has no one to answer
to. There is no feast or wedding but she makes part of the
company, and she needs no invitation. She has plenty to eat
and to drink. She lacks only one thing: that rod to chase
away the pain in her bottom. And this she searches for and
runs after.

She cannot bear the sight of her children and pecks at them
the way a hen pecks at her chicks when she is kneeling before
the cock. She puts them away from her, becomes a sort of
bogeyman for them. Often she makes wax candles and she
habitually offers great numbers of them so that God may rid
her of her children or that the plague may take them. "Because of them," she says, "I cannot find anyone who will have
me. No one would get mixed up in this." And she takes to
beating them and knocking them about; she slaps them and
scratches them and bites them and calls down the plague on
them. Because she does not have the love of a man, the
children must pay.

This she does and a great deal more. If she has scraped
some money together, she carries it about with her and says
that this very morning a man came to her door to pay it to
her. Then she speaks of Robert or Martin, who still owe her
money, seven times what she has just collected, and who will

[149]

pay her soon, perhaps in two weeks. To hear her tell it, she is very rich.

If she meets a gossip, someone who likes to go about repeating what she hears, she sidles up to her and says: "There is something bothering me. I'm a very good friend of yours —for you're not stupid or proud—I've always liked you, and for a long time I've been meaning to ask you to come for a walk with me. I know you won't mind if I chat with you a little, because I'm sure we must be related, or so my mother used to say. But my heart is full of grief for my husband whom I have lost. My friends have forbidden me to put off my mourning, because I couldn't gain anything by doing so. And certainly my husband was very good to me. He gave me a great many things, both shoes and dresses. He made me mistress of himself and of his property. He was a very decent sort, but he wasn't much good in bed. As soon as he got into bed, he would turn his behind on me; and he would sleep that way all night. That was all the pleasure I had. It used to make me very unhappy.

"Of course, I can't deny that he was a very wealthy man before I married him. But he was already quite bald when he came my way, and I was just a little girl with a dirty little face. You were only a baby then, running about like a little chick after your mother, who was a good friend of my mother's—they were close relatives. I swear by Our Savior, I am so grieved at his death! But one thing about my husband, he was a good provider; he knew how to rake in the money and how to save it, may his soul rest in peace! I have plenty of kettles and pots and white quilts and good beds and chests and chairs; and bonnets and coats and furs, which he had made in great quantity. Also I have plenty of sheets, both linen and woolen, and two kinds of firewood, the large and the small. My house is not exactly bare; I certainly have lovely kitchen equipment; I still have two caldrons, one made in the old style with the edges turned all around it—my husband set great value on it. But I don't care to brag about what God has given me.

"You know Dieudonné very well? And you know Herbert well and Baudouin, Gombert's son? Do you know anything about their situations? I'm being pushed to marry again. But it's amazing about people: you imagine there is wealth where there is scarcely enough to eat. Many people are deep in debt, but I am truly rich. You can see the bark of the tree, but you can't tell what lies underneath. A great deal so-called wealth is mostly wind, but mine is there to see. I make lots of sheets every year. I'm an honest woman and well brought up. The best people hereabouts often come calling on me. Some of them are relatives of yours. But I don't want to drop names. Are you related to Gomer? But as for Gomer, well, I won't say any more about him.

"But let me tell you something, my dear friend. Last year I went to a fortune teller, and he made me lie down flat in the middle of a circle, and he looked me over, and he said I would yet have a young man. Do you know of any worthy men in your neighborhood? The one who lives next door to you seems like a very intelligent fellow. He gave me such a look the other day! But I was on my guard and took good care not to look back. A man who lives at Tournai and who is related to me on my father's side spoke to me of a friend of his, a very rich, propertied gentleman, who lives close by him. But he's old, they tell me, and I've come to despise him of late. I swear by Saint Leonard I will never take an old man!

Because when it comes to getting a little bed exercise, I've no mind to go without seed and take the chaff. I have enough property to get a handsome young man.

"Dear friend, think of me if there is any honest, sensible fellow among your acquaintance; he would be well matched with me. Now be nice and smart, and if you can find something for me, so may God pardon me, you will have a good reward. I don't like making promises or getting involved, but of one thing you can be sure: if this business turns out well, you will be a very well-dressed woman. Look around in the Chausée and Neufbourg sections of Valenciennes or at Anzin. Who is this son of Dame Wiborc and of Geoffrey? The day before yesterday when they proposed Isabel to him, he gave them the cold shoulder. But if you don't mind, perhaps you might speak to him secretly.

"But I've been here such a long time! I would stay the night, but I'm afraid of putting you out. Let's make an appointment for Sunday. Clemence will come too, and we'll have some apples and nuts and some of that wine from Laenois; and I'll tell you about that relative of mine—he doesn't live far from here—who wants to make a nun of me." Then she gives her a tap with the back of her hand and turns away and goes home The other one goes her way and repeats what she has heard everywhere.

Meanwhile, this is how the widow fares: her hairy Goliath so pricks and excites her and the fire burns so high in her that at last she succeeds in getting a man. And when she has caught him in her trap, he can really complain of being worn out. Though he may know his way about those tender netherparts, though he be lively and quick and can well strike and plunge, he will still be despised in the morning. No one can help him there; he will get rough treatment.

As soon as the lady gets out of bed, she kicks the cat off the hearth. Then all sorts of ill feelings come out, scoldings, reproaches: "What have I got under my roof?—a poor thing, a wretch, a softling. Aie! God must hate me! That I, who disdained proper young men, gallants and gentlemen, that I should take up with such a born weakling! May all who deal in such deceits have bad luck! And after putting me to such torments! All he wants to do is eat and sleep. All night long he snores like a pig. That's his delight and his pastime. Am I not ill treated then? When I stretch out next to him all naked and he turns away from me, it almost tears the heart out of me. My husband, my lord, you never treated me that way. You called me your sweet beloved, and so I called you too, because you turned toward me and kissed me sweetly and said to begin with: 'My beautiful wife and lady, what a sweet breath you have!' Husband, those were your very words. May your soul rest in heaven! And this vagabond treats me like the dung in his barnyard. But I well know, by Saint Loy, that his morals are no better than those of an Albigensian heretic. He doesn't care about loving women."

To which the man replies: "Lady, you are mistaken. You have such a wry face that I find it hard to touch you. And I cannot keep my agreement with you. Goliath gapes too often. I can't satisfy him; I'm likely to die before I do."

"Lying coward!" says the lady. "You ought to be a monk and enter a monastery. You have served me badly. Oh, it is easy to see that I was not in my right mind when I gave up John, with his property, good tillable land, and Geoffrey and Gilbert and Baudouin and Foucuin, and took the worst man from here to Beauvais. Oh, husband, you are ill replaced! You deserve to be deeply mourned, for never was there a better man than you. Alas! that all your good qualities should be gone with you: your wisdom and your knowledge, your good manners and your kindness! You were always kind and submissive. Never did you curse me or beat me or give me an ill word. Whereas this whelp threatens me. It's only right that I hate him."

The young man answers angrily: "Lady, you have a greedy mouth in you that too often demands to be fed. It has tired my poor old war-horse out. I've just withdrawn him all shrunken and sore. One cannot work so much without getting weary and limp. The peasant may be a good worker, but not every day is a working day. You can drive the mare so hard as not to leave a drop of blood or saliva in her. You have so milked and drained me that I am half dead, and half mad too. I'll tell you straight out: a man must have a tough skin indeed to let the devil trick him into taking a widow with children, for he will never have a moment's peace thereafter. Come on then, my sour old girl, give me the thirty marks you promised me on Tuesday or I won't do any more of this back-humping work. But by Saint Richier, if I don't get them, you'll pay dearly."

When she hears her young man ask for money, the good woman is furious. She sends him to all the devils in hell. She would sooner he beat her or killed her than that she should hand over that sum; he'll not have a single mark of her money. She begins once more to curse him and to quarrel and say foul things. "Ah, wastrel!" she cries. "All my goods are wasted. You have so bled me and robbed me that I no longer have a stick of firewood nor a grain of wheat. My house has been swept clean. You're a heavy burden to bear. And we know your family well—the stinking wretches—and your sisters and your aunts, who are all dirty whores. . . ."

At these words the young man leaps up, and without so

much as a by-your-leave he grabs her by the haunches and gives her such a thrashing, more than she bargained for, that he soon pays her in full for her foul words. Then he leaps on her again and beats and pounds her with his fists until he is all in a sweat and worn out. When she has had enough, the widow runs and hides in her chamber, without hat or headdress. She has been so roughly handled in the fray that her hair is all disheveled. She goes to bed and covers up, forbids anyone to come in, and lies there licking her wounds.

But in the end she calls out: "Oh, you thief, how you have hurt me! Now may God grant me a quick death and bring me where I can be with my husband. May my soul follow his and may I abide with him. For there is nothing I want more, dear husband, than to be with you." And she speaks in an affectedly weak voice as though she were really dying; for she knows how to make the most of her wounds. Then after a while, she begins to speak up a little; she calls for hot broth, for cheese tarts, for little cakes. Also she takes a great many baths, morning and even, early and late, until she is all healed and cured. Then, the quarrel over, the two of them come back together again.

For one thing I have learned is that if a man knows how to swing his balls he can overcome all ills. Where such a man lives, there the cat is commended to God—no one beats it or lays a hand on it; there the cushions are plumped up and the benches pushed against the wall, so that the man may not hurt himself on them; there not a log remains on the hearth; there is he loved and served and given everything he wants— chicken and other fowl; there is he lord and master; there is he washed and combed and his hair parted. For I tell you once again, according to the proverb: she who would have her husband soothe her tail must pile endearments on his head.

You who despise women, think of those endearments in that hour when she is under you and you on top. He who would experience that joy must give up to his beloved a great part of his will, no matter how much it grieves him to do so. A man who is not distressed from time to time is neither kind nor honest. For if my wife scolds and says nasty things to me, all I need do is leave and she stops. Anyone who tried to answer her would be reasoning with madness. And it is better for me to go away than to hit her with a piece of wood. Lords, you who are submissive, deceitful, and blusterers, do not be dismayed in any way: submissive men have more joy than do those quarrelsome rascals who are always looking for a fight. And finally, Gautier le Leu says that he who will oppress his wife or quarrel with her only because she wants what all her neighbors want does not have a gentle heart. But I do not choose to go any deeper into this question. A woman only does what she must. The tale is done. Set up the drinks.

Along with Jean Bodel, the most prolific rhymer of fabliaux was Gautier le Leu, who composed in all eleven fabliaux of which eight are preserved today. Concerning the life of Gautier, the only available information is that supplied by the works themselves, for, as in the case of Rutebeuf, no contemporary document bears his name. The extensive literary sources for his works, however, lead us to suppose that he was well known in his day. The prologue to his fabliau "Le Prestre Teint" ("The Painted Priest," not included in this collection) makes it likely that Gautier was one of the innumerable wandering clerics, the *vagantes,* of thirteenth-century France, probably both author and performer of his works. It is also quite possible, as some passages from his works suggest, that he was formerly a student at the schools of Orleans. Gautier certainly knew Latin and most probably had a liberal education; allusions in his works also show his wide acquaintance with French literature of his day. It has even been argued that he was associated with the Benedictine Abbey of Maroilles and that, having fallen into difficulty with the Church, he developed a violent hatred of priests.

In his entire production Gautier was an extraordinary stylist, displaying a wide and varied vocabulary; the essential characteristics of his work are a crudeness of expression, a violent and bold obscenity, biting satire, and a cynical and profoundly pessimistic turn of mind: in fine, a good example of the thirteenth-century jongleur precariously living by his wits.

Although it is a fabliau in spirit, "La Veuve" is not a story in the strict sense of the word, but rather a *tableau de moeurs* in which is traced with painful accuracy the state of mind of a widow suddenly deprived of the comforts of sex. The work is best seen in the light of the so-called "quarrel concerning women" which raged from the time of Saint Jerome (c. 340–420) to the end of the Renaissance. This conflict resulted from the prevalence of two diametrically opposed attitudes toward love and woman, the one idealistic and courtly, the other satiric and vehement.

The portrait of the widow in this story, like that of so many other women in the fabliaux and of their literary cousins, the old woman in Jean de Meung's *Roman de la Rose* (*The Romance of the Rose;* thirteenth century) and Chaucer's "Wife of Bath," is a prime example of the antifeminist position. Gautier le Leu's widow resembles to some extent the widow in Marie de France's "The Woman Who Hanged Her Husband's Body," as she is shown at the beginning of the tale, but this fabliau develops along completely different lines when the widow returns from her husband's funeral. Both tales, however, stress the inconstancy of women's emotions. A more closely similar portrait of a widow, and one which perhaps drew on Gautier's fabliau, is that in the second book of the *Lamenta* (*Lamentations*) by Matthew, called the Bigamist, a thirteenth-century writer and cleric who was dismissed by the Church because of his marriage to a widow. In this passage, elaborated by Jehan Lefevre in his translation, *Lamentations de Matheolus* (The Lamentations of Matthew; 1370), the widow is urged to remarry, quarrels with her children, and finally finds a second husband, who loses no time in squandering her savings. Similarly, the fourteenth "joy" in the *Quinze Joyes de Mariage* (*Fifteen Joys of Marriage,* often attributed to Antoine de la Sale), the most scathing satire on women written in the fifteenth century, portrays in outrageously obscene language the excessive sexual demands made by a widow on her second husband. The popularity of the theme continued to spread during the Renaissance throughout most of western Europe, and the widow as portrayed by Gautier le Leu became a stock figure until La Fontaine, in his tale "La Jeune Veuve" ("The Young Widow"), fixed forever, and in exquisite form, her literary character.

Edition: Charles H. Livingston, *Le Jongleur Gautier le Leu* (Cambridge, Mass., 1951), pp. 165–183.

COVETOUSNESS
AND ENVY

by Jean Bodel

My lords, having told many invented tales, I should like now to tell a true one. For the man who can tell only fables, that is to say, he who cannot tell the truth as well as he can lie, is no true storyteller and is not worthy to serve at an important court; but the man who is proud of his trade rightfully should make one wise tale for every two vain ones.

Now it is certain truth that once, more than a hundred years ago, there were two friends who led a very bad life. For one was so full of envy that no one was more envious than he; and the other was so covetous that nothing could satisfy him. They were truly bad men and worse than bad: for covetousness leads to usury and makes men give short weight

[159]

so they may get greater riches; and envy is still worse, for it is a plague to everyone.

Now one day Covetousness and Envy rode out together, and, as I have been told, they came upon Saint Martin in an open field. And he had been in their company but a short while when he put them to the test to sound the ill will in their hearts. They came upon two well-traveled roads separated by a chapel, and there Saint Martin said to these men of evil life: "My lords, at that church I shall turn off to the right, and I would leave you better off than when I met you. I am the worthy Saint Martin. If one of you will ask a gift of me, at once he shall have whatever he desires; and the one who keeps silent will immediately get twice as much as the other."

Then the covetous one thought that he would allow his fellow to ask, and so he would get twice as much as he did, for he was greedy for the double gift. "Dear companion," he said, "do you ask, and surely you will get whatever you ask for. Let your wish be generous, for if you know how to make the best of it you will be rich all your life." But he whose heart was full of envy refused to make his wish, for he would have died of envy and sadness if the other had got more than he. So the two of them remained a great while without asking.

"What are you waiting for?" said the covetous one. "Are you afraid it will turn out badly for you? I'll get twice as much as you do; you can't prevent it. Now ask! or I'll beat you worse than ever an ass was beaten crossing a bridge."

"Sir," the envious one answered, "before you do me any harm, know that I will ask. But if I ask for money and wealth you will get twice as much as I. You will get nothing if I can help it.

"Saint Martin," he said, "I ask that I may lose one of my eyes and my companion both of his. Thus will he be doubly afflicted."

At once his eye was put out. The bargain was well kept: out of four eyes they lost three, and they gained nothing more besides. So Saint Martin made one of them one-eyed and the other blind, and by their own wish they lost. Bad luck, I say, to him who pities them, for they were of evil character.

This story of "Le Couvoiteus et l'envieus" is of Eastern provenance. It was very popular in the sermon literature of medieval Europe and is included in collections of moral tales, such as the *Exempla* (No. 196) of Jacques de Vitry (ca. 1178–1240), the fourteenth-century Spanish *Libro de los Exemplos* (*Book of Exempla*), the *Enseignement Trebor* (*Instructions of Trebor*), a fourteenth-century manual written by Robert de Ho (*Trebor* is an anagram) for the instruction of his son.

Saint Martin, who was a patron saint of drinking bouts in the Middle Ages, was well known as the granter of wishes with ironically unfortunate consequences. At least two other extant fabliaux exploit the same theme: "Les Quatre Sohais Saint Martin" ("The Four Wishes of Saint Martin") and "Les Sohais" ("The Wishes"), the latter by Gautier le Leu. The theme of the ironically granted wish has remained popular and is used in folk and fairy tales, as well as in such literary works as Balzac's *La Peau de Chagrin* and that favorite of amateur theater, *The Monkey's Paw* by W. W. Jacobs. (On Jean Bodel, see the note on "Brunain, the Priest's Cow.")

Edition: Reid, pp. 5–7.

THE ABUNDANCE

May God help us, who governs everything! Some years ago, about the time that Acre was taken (I have all the facts of this matter), it happened in a tavern that a young man from Normandy, where many fine men go begging, wanted to break his fast one morning; but he had neither hen nor chick nor anything at all that was worth eating, except a single halfpenny loaf of bread. He had one penny in his hand, and he asked the tavern keeper to draw him a penny's worth of wine. This tavern keeper, who was very haughty, proud, and quarrelsome and who put on airs and prided himself on his elegance, went straight to the barrel and drew a full measure. He put a tankard in the Norman's hand and said: "Here! Let's go! Quickly!" And he poured so precipitously into the tankard which the Norman held out that, through pride and ill temper, he spilled half the wine.

When the Norman saw what he'd lost, he was full to the brim with rage; for he had only one penny left. He cried to the tavern keeper: "Sir lord, I have no need of your haughtiness!" And the other answered him: "Go your way, you crazy fool! You may have good luck at the Second Coming. For it is said that he who spills wine will profit by it and have great abundance. You should be pleased at the loss. The wine isn't far away; I'll draw some more. Don't talk to me about such a loss. I have spilled many a mug and never paid it any heed at all. I wouldn't complain so much about a keg as you do about a half pint."

The Norman heard this, and it didn't suit him at all that the tavern keeper made fun of him; he would rather have been in Spain than to have such a cause for anger. He took a halfpenny out of his purse and told the tavern keeper to go quickly and fetch him half a cheese. "Very well," said he; and he went straight up out of the wine cellar. The Norman went to the barrel and, without regard to consequences, pulled out the spigot and let the wine run out on the ground.

The tavern keeper wasn't long in finding the cheese, and when he returned and saw his wine spilled his heart swelled with rage and chagrin. But before he said a word to the Norman or laid a hand on him, he went to plug up the barrel. When he had replaced the spigot, he came and berated the Norman for his villainous behavior. He grabbed him by the skirt of his coat and told him that he would either make good for the wine or he would have him hanged on the spot. The Norman said: "Let me be! I've never seen anyone crazier than you. Don't you remember telling me I would profit and have great abundance because of the little bit of my wine you spilled? Well now, in truth, you should profit a hundredfold; for you can bathe in your wine that is streaming over the cellar. Soon you will be able to make quite a splash with the profit that is right there before you. Let me be, for I tell you, and your own words bear me out, that your needs will all be fulfilled. This is the truth as you taught it to me."

Then the tavern keeper seized him and held him hard. But the Norman was big and strong; he threw the other so hard against a barrel that he almost brained him. The barrel rack gave way, the barrels came loose, and three hoops were broken. All the wine measures fell down and all the mugs were broken. In some places in that cellar you could have bathed in wine. Then they compounded the damage. The tavern keeper struggled violently, but the Norman wedged him between two flowing spigots, and he would have choked him to death there if the neighbors had not come in. They came to the tavern keeper's aid, and they struck out at the Norman; but not one of them really laid a hand on him. Nevertheless, they made a great deal of trouble for him and, willy-nilly, brought him before the king.

This was Count Henry of Champagne, who held that land in fief. When this complaint was brought before him, the tavern keeper told him all that had happened and how shamefully the Norman had behaved to him; and he demanded restitution of all he had lost. The king called on the Norman and ordered him to tell him the truth. "I will not tell the least lie," said he. And at once he told him the story just as you have heard it here, for he would not stoop to deny a single word. The king asked the tavern keeper if what the Norman said was true. "Yes, sire," he said, "every word, for he has not told a single lie." When the king's men heard this, they clapped their hands and laughed. They all said to King Henry that never had such a fine trick been recounted in the royal presence. And because he made them laugh so much, they all favored the Norman. And so the king answered: "He who lost is the loser."

The anonymous "La Plantez" is the oldest fabliau that can be dated with any certainty. It must have been composed between 1191, the date of the fall of Saint-Jean-d'Acre mentioned as a recent event in line 2, and 1197, the year of the death of Henry of Champagne, King of Jerusalem, at whose court the cause was pleaded. The intrigue, of the simplest kind, turns about a precept which, like that in "Brunain, the Priest's Cow," is taken at face value. As in many other fabliaux, proverbs are the central motif around which the action revolves: the tavern keeper's haughty dictum, "He who spills wine will profit by it," is matched by the king's judgment: "He who loses, is the loser"— or, in modern terms, "Don't cry over spilt milk."

There are no known analogues to "The Abundance," and the only imitation seems to be by Barthélemy Imbert, who in his *Choix de Fabliaux Mis en Vers* (*Selected Fabliaux Put into Rhyme;* Paris, 1788, 2 vols.) put into modern verse the adaptation of this fabliau made by Legrand d'Aussy in 1779.

Edition: Montaiglon-Raynaud, III, 170–174.

THE LAY OF ARISTOTLE

by Henri d'Andeli

One ought not to refrain from repeating
good stories, since they allow us to take in by our ears good
sense and good manners, things which, as is right and proper,
rejoice good men. But bad men become ill-humored as soon
as they hear such things said; and just as good men esteem
other good men, so do the wicked despise and slander them,

if they can do no worse. For envy is of such a nature that it invades the hearts of envious men and so takes them that they cannot hear a good word without wanting to contradict it. I marvel at how envy oppresses them. You wicked and ungentle men, why do you load your own slanders and discontents on other men's shoulders? It is a wicked thing to do, for in doing it you are guilty of two mortal sins: first of slander and then of false witness. Certainly this is a cruel and a base way to behave. But no one can stop envy, and I do not wish to be delayed here in the attempt. I do not think it is worth my while to reprehend those cruel scoundrels, whom one might call Ganelons and who could not refrain from slander even if they died for it, they are so set on it and so accustomed to it.

Let me then return to my subject, a story that I have undertaken to tell because I prized it greatly when I heard it and felt that it should be made known and put into rhyme, a tale without scandal or baseness. For a work which runs to baseness ought not to be heard at court. Never in my life have I stirred up any such filth in my works and never do I mean to do so. I have never repeated an evil word in any of my tales, for grossness disfigures everything and takes away all pleasure. Nor do I, as long as I live, wish to be the inventor of anything that smacks of baseness, but I will make my tales after the true originals, things that are both pleasant and profitable, as fruits and spices are.

The king of Greece, Alexander, who was of such great majesty that he had in his anger overthrown and abased many princes, while he himself waxed ever greater and rose higher, in his reign made Generosity his minister, which was hard on the avaricious folk but good for the liberal ones. For as the avaricious love money, so do the generous hate to keep it, knowing that no good can come of it as long as it is under lock and key. So nothing bought with silver or gold had any power over Alexander; rather, all his treasure was in his knights. Other princes are not like that; they all pinch and save, and hide and hoard their wealth, for they have no honor other than wealth. He who was called Alexander gathered wealth only to distribute it; he got it quickly, held it but a short time, and soon gave it away. For he had given the reins to Generosity in order to enhance his own power.

But let me return to my tale.

This king of Greece and of Egypt had recently reduced to subjection the greater part of India, and in that country he remained and settled down. If you ask me why he stayed there, living quietly, I can easily tell you the reason: Love, which is quick to take hold and embrace, quick to seize and to bind, held him in bondage, so that he had become a devoted lover—without regret, for he had found a mistress as beautiful as could be wished for. He had no desire to go plead his case elsewhere, but only to stay where he was and to be with her. Love is such a king and such a master that he can make the most powerful man in the world so humble and obedient, that he takes no thought for himself but bends his will to another's. It is true that Love is of such worth that once he has taken a man by surprise that man should in no way rebel against him. For, truth to tell, Love has as much right over a king as he has over the poorest man in Champagne or in France, so absolute is his dominion.

The king remained with his mistress, and they exchanged many and many a sweet word until he became so mad about her and lived so foolishly that he could not help himself or stir a step without her. This was the will of Love and of her who had pierced him with a burning spark; with a burning spark she pierced him and so made him her subject. Nevertheless, she did not come off unscathed. The game was so evenly matched that I cannot tell who was better at it; for the girl herself was as inflamed with love as it is possible to be. It was no wonder that he lingered there, for he was guided by his desire, and he had to heed it or else disobey the rules which Love has laid down for all true lovers.

His courtiers did not dare speak up about these matters, but secretly they buzzed their disapproval until his tutor Aristotle came to hear of it. And it was entirely proper that he should try to dissuade Alexander from his love. He gave him a fine lecture and told him that it was wrong for him to abandon the young knights of his realm for one wanton woman.

"How many then should I love?" said Alexander. "I think that they who call me mad for this cannot love at all. For a man can love only one woman, and truly he cannot please more than one. And he who bears me a grudge because I do what my heart entreats me to do has little love in his own heart."

Aristotle, who knew everything of true learning that was to be known, replied to the king that it was considered a great shame that he should insist on behaving the way he did, spending his whole week with his mistress and providing no entertainment or feasts for his knights. "Sire," said Aristotle to his master, "I believe that you are quite blind and that you could be led to pasture with the other dumb beasts. Your mind must be deranged if for some strange girl you have so utterly changed that one can find no vestige of reason in you. I beg and beseech you to give up this manner of life or you will pay dear for it." So did Aristotle admonish his lord for the love he bore him. And the king replied, courteously and shamefacedly, as though he were entirely at Aristotle's disposal, that he would indeed overcome his love for the lady.

And Alexander stood by his word; for many hours and many days, because of his tutor's chiding and reproach, he did not visit or go near his love. But his desire grew no weaker; indeed, though he refrained from going to her, he loved her and desired her more now than he ever had before. Fear of wrongdoing made him keep his word, but he had not put out of mind what he put out of sight. The God of Love recalled to his memory her bright face, her lovely form, in which there was no trace of ugliness or evil, her smooth brow, clearer than crystal, her fair body, her beautiful mouth, and her blond head.

"Ah!" he cried. "In what great distress everyone wants me to live! My tutor would have me struggle against what lies in my heart. I am so cramped and enslaved by the will of others that I am mad with it. It seems to me madness to suffer so because others wish it. My master Aristotle and all my men together do not feel what I feel, and if I continue to submit to them I am lost entirely. Does the God of Love live by the rules? Not he, but by his own will."

Thus did the king lament. And then he returned to her who so pleased and delighted him. The maiden, all forlorn at his absence, jumped to her feet to meet the king. And she said to him: "Sire, I was aware of your great distress. How can a true lover bear to be absent from what he holds dear?" With that she wept and was silent. The king replied: "My love, don't wonder at my having stayed away, for there was a reason for it. My knights and barons reproached me exceedingly for so rarely keeping them company, and my tutor scolded me severely for it. I know I have done wrong for his sake to disobey the will of my true love, but I was afraid of shame and dishonor."

"Sire," said the lady, "by my salvation, I know what this business means. But if art and cunning do not fail me, I will so avenge myself on your pale old tutor that you will be able to catch him in a worse fault than your own and reproach him for it. That will I do if I can but live till noon tomorrow and if Love, who will never fail in strength, will let loose his power. His logic and his grammar will do him no good against me. He will be a skillful fencer indeed if, now that I have made up my mind, Mother Nature does not subdue him through me. And this you will see tomorrow. If Your Majesty will get up early, he will see how Nature proceeds against your tutor to despoil him of his wits and learning. He has never been struck by such an ingenious and cutting whip as he will feel tomorrow if only I can come before his window in the morning. He'll be sorry that he abused and tricked you. So be on the watch from the windows of this tower, and I shall make my preparations."

Alexander was astonished by what she said. He embraced her hard and spoke to her pleasantly: "How precious you are, my true and gentle heart! If I love anyone but you, may God not receive me in paradise. I have just the love I desire; I want no part of any others." So he left his love and went away, while she remained there.

In the morning, at the proper time and hour, the fair, blond maiden arose, and rising was no pain to her. Then she went into the garden below the tower, dressed in nothing but her shift, a tunic dotted with violet, for it was a summer morning, the orchard was all green, and she had no fear of cold, the weather being warm and a gentle breeze blowing. Nature had endowed her bright countenance with the rose and the lily; in all her figure there was nothing that did not rightly belong there. And do not think that she had a wimple or band about her head; her beautiful tresses, long and blond, set off her loveliness. Her fair head had no need of trimming. She played there in the orchard in the colors nature had given her. Barefoot, bareheaded, ungirdled, she went her way, raising the skirts of her tunic and singing in a low voice:

> There just beneath the olive tree,
> *There, there I see her come, my love!*
> There the spring flows limpidly,
> And the iris grow in the alder grove.
> *Oh, see her, see her there, oh see*
> *the lovely blond maid who taketh me!*

The king at the tower window listens to her song with ear and heart and takes pleasure both in her words and in her music. Before the day is out, his tutor, Aristotle of Athens, will be persuaded that love which is constant, worthy, and loyal should be encouraged. And he will never more distress the king or reproach him for being in love, for he will learn of the madness in himself and be drunk with desire.

Aristotle, who had arisen and was seated at his books, saw the lady come and go, and a yearning seized his heart, making him close his books. "Ah, God!" he said. "If now this beauty should come closer, I would place myself in her power. What! would I let her have power over me? No! It has never yet happened to me, I who know so much and have such powers, that the folly in my heart has betrayed me to a single glance. The God of Love seeks my hospitality. But my honor puts him to shame. What a guest and what a lodging that would be! Alas! what has happened to my wits? I am old and gray, bleached and black and pale and skinny, more zealous in philosophy than anyone I know or could imagine. I have labored well and hard, and still I pursue learning. Now Love, who has snared many a worthy man, makes me ignorant the better to capture me. In learning I have lost my knowledge, in knowledge I have lost my learning. But since Love proceeds against me and since I cannot defend myself, let come what may and let justice take its course; let it not be said that I have stood in its way. Come, Love, invade me! Now come to me! I do not know what else to say, since I am unable to prevent it."

While the tutor was lamenting, the lady was making a chaplet of many and various flowers. As she did so, she thought of love, and she sang while she picked the flowers:

> *Love, lie still where my heart beats!*
> The pretty maid was washing her sheets.
> Fair one, I love you too much!
> *Love, lie still where my heart beats!*
> *Where I my bosom touch.*

So she sang and so she played. But Aristotle was very much grieved that she came no nearer. She knew well what was needed to inflame and entice him. The arrow she would shoot at him must be cunningly feathered. She worked so well and took such pains that at last she bent him to her will. She put the chaplet on her blond head, and, the better to deceive and enchant him, pretended to be all unaware that Aristotle could see her. Not caring that he too concealed his feelings, for she had put her all into this affair, she drew near his window, singing a verse of a weaving song:

> In a garden by a little stream,
> Whose waters over bright sands gleam,

A king's daughter sits and her woes tells over,
While sighing she calls on her sweet lover:
Ah! fair Count Guise,
Your love has bereft me of laughter and ease.

When Master Aristotle heard her sing so close to his window, which was a low one, he felt that he had suffered enough, and he seized hold of her. She pretended to be frightened and cried: "Ah, God! Who stops me?" "You are welcome here, lady," said he who was steward and servant of the folly that commanded him. "Master," said the lady. "Alas! Is it you whom I see here?" "Yes," said he, "my sweet love. For you I would risk everything, body and life and honor. Love and Nature have so moved me that I cannot bear to part from you."

"Ah, tutor," said she, "since you love me so much, it's not I who will ever blame you for it. But things are going badly. I don't know who it was that embroiled me with the king and chided him for spending so much time with me."

Then said Aristotle: "Never mind. For I can put down all the ill will and reproofs and the shouting and strife. For the king loves and fears me more than he does any of his other followers. But for God's sake come into the house and appease my desires with your smooth and lovely body."

"Ah, tutor," she said, "before I yield to your folly, you must, if you are so stricken with love, consent to do a strange thing for me. For I have been seized with a great desire to ride astride you over the grass in this garden. And I want you to wear a saddle, for so I shall ride more respectably."

The old man replied joyfully that he would do that willingly and as one who belonged to her entirely. The God of Love must really have overwhelmed him to make him carry a palfrey's saddle on his shoulder into the garden. You can imagine how mad he looked carrying it. And she busied herself to put it on his back. Love can indeed work miracles with an old codger, since Nature so commands, if he can cause the greatest scholar in the world to be saddled like an old nag and crawl on all fours over the grass. (Here I ought to provide a proverb and point a moral, and I shall do so at the proper time.) He let the girl get up on his back and so he carried her. And Alexander rejoiced to see him who had not been able to keep his wits or prevent Love from making a fool of him.

The lady drove him happily through the garden and riding she sang loud and clear:

> *As love leads so he goes.*
> Lovely Doe is washing clothes.
> Master Silly carries me.
> *As love leads so he goes,*
> *Whom good love holds in fee.*

"Tutor," said the king, "where are you off to? I see that you are being ridden. What! Are you out of your mind? Who has brought you to this? Once you absolutely forbade me to see her, and now she has brought you to such a state that there is no reason in you and you behave like a beast."

Aristotle lifted his head and made the lady get down. Then, all ashamed, he replied: "Sire, you speak the truth. But you can see I was right to be afraid that you, in the prime of your youth, would consume yourself, since I, who am full of years, could make no stand against Love, who has brought me to this sorry state which you see. All that I have read and learned Love has turned to nothing in a single hour."

Then the king was happy. Laughing, he pardoned his tutor.

And his tutor let him alone to do as he wished, for he had no reason to restrain him.

Well, there is one question I would like to ask about this business, for which I cite Cato, who is the first authority on it: *Turpe est doctori, cum culpa redarguit ipsum.* So Cato says, and these verses are my gloss: He is a fool who reproves another for a thing in which he allows himself to be caught. And he who does so reduces his own worth. So Aristotle chided his lord and thought ill of him for being so much in love, and then was so stirred by love himself that he could make no resistance to it. Thus did Love constrain him and carnal desire, which has power over every man and woman. So it seems to me that the tutor was not guilty of any offense, for he did not do wrong by reason of his learning, but because of Nature, true and absolute.

So Henry declares this story ended; and in its conclusion it shows that a true heart cannot be estranged.

"Le Lai d'Aristote" is unique in this collection in that it depicts historical personages. The Aristotle of this medieval story, however, is wise only by reputation; in action he is a moralizing old fool. The tale is a humorous testimony to the power of love and an ingenious restatement of the conventional literary theme of the sage debased by the cunning of woman.

The anecdote from which the fabliau derives doubtless had nothing to do with either Aristotle or Alexander. Different protagonists appear in several early Sanskrit versions, one in the pre-Christian *Pantchatantra* (*The Five Books*), and also in an Arabic analogue. It is generally assumed that Henri d'Andeli's version, written around 1220 and preserved in five manuscripts of the thirteenth century, was the first to introduce the Macedonian emperor and his famous tutor into a traditional tale of Eastern provenance. The popularity of this fabliau was immense in the later Middle Ages, to judge from the number of iconographic representations of the philosopher with saddle and bridle—for example, a famous one on the cathedral of Rouen. Also, a number of medieval authors, notably Adam de la Hall and the Italian Brunetto Latini, mention the story. One fourteenth-century writer, Jean Bras de Fer, in his *Pamphile et Galathée* (*Pamphilus and Galatea;* ca. 1330) inveighs vehemently against the credence given by the unlettered to this scandalous story of dubious authenticity.

Later reworkings of the story in the Middle Ages and the Renaissance further attest its popularity in western Europe. It was used in a sermon, "De Aristotile et Uxori Alexandri" ("Aristotle and the Wife of Alexander"), by Jacques de Vitry (ca. 1178–1240) and afterward was incorporated into other popular collections of *exempla,* stories for the use of preachers, designed to enliven and point the morals of sermons. In 1774 Barthélemy Imbert adapted it in a rhymed version which was the basis of a comic opera composed in 1780 and of a play by Alphonse Daudet produced in 1878. In Germany it became the subject of numerous compositions: toward the end of the thirteenth century Ulrich von Eschenbach used it in his *Alexandreis,* and in the same period it appeared as the Middle High German tale *"Aristoteles und Fillis";* thereafter it appeared in the *Weltkronik* (*World Chronicle;* 1394) of Heinz Sentlinger, in a sixteenth-century version from the *Fastnachtspiele* (Shrovetide plays), and in a play by Hans Sachs in 1574, and, finally, again as a play by Kannegiesser in 1810. It took its place in the famous German collection of stories, the *Gesammtabenteuer* (1850), and it passed into the literature of most of the countries of Europe, including England.

This fabliau is written in a style more like that of the courtly tale than of the fabliau. The author begins with an attack against slanderers and a condemnation of vulgarity in literature, and the tale which follows consistently avoids all coarseness and is remarkable for its Ovidian sophistication and elegance. It was the author's fear of coarseness which caused him to call his poem a "lay" rather than a "fabliau," a term that had come to denote a work of erotic subject matter and bawdy treatment. However, it is precisely because of his tale's erotic and humorous nature that today it is called a fabliau.

The Henri who claims the tale in its closing lines has been definitely identified as the well-known author Henri d'Andeli, who lived in the first half of the thirteenth century. Most probably he came from the Norman village of Andelys, although his literary activity centered in Paris, where he was a student at the university. Henri is the author of several other works in French: the allegorical "La Bataille des Sept Arts" ("The Battle of the Seven Arts"), a work about the university quarrels of the 1230's; "Le Dit du Chancelier Philippe" ("On Chancellor Philip"), a rhymed funeral eulogy on the Chancellor of the University of Paris who died in 1236; and "La Bataille des Vins" ("The Battle of Wines"), an amusing and lively piece ostensibly based on a scene at the court of the French king Philip Augustus.

Edition: Maurice Delbouille, *Le Lai d'Aristote de Henri d'Andeli* (Paris, 1951).

Manuscript of *La Borgoise d'Orliens,* lines 1–66, from the collection of the Bibliothèque Nationale, Paris.

AFTERWORD

Fablel sont bon a escouter;
Maint duel, maint mal font mesconter
Et maint anui et maint meffet.

Montaiglon-Raynaud, I, 70

"I can recite tales and fabliaux," boasts a jongleur of the mid-thirteenth century. The tales, he goes on to say, are "of Perceval, of Charlemagne and Roland, the Romance of Renard . . . and all the feudal epics." Thus, at an early date, a distinct group of Old French works, the fabliaux, are attested as occupying a prominent and popular place alongside the great medieval epic, the *Song of Roland,* the stories of Reynard the Fox, and the mysterious *Romance of the Grail* of Chrétien de Troyes. But although these last works have been studied and enjoyed, not only by specialists of medieval literature but by the general public, the fabliaux have remained practically unknown outside a restricted circle of philologists and students of Old French. This obscurity is undeserved. The art of the fabliau achieved a success lasting well over 150 years, and it exerted a great influence on the literature of Western Europe for centuries thereafter.

As the name implies, the fabliau has something in common with the fable, of which word it is merely a diminutive form. The term was invented by the authors who composed these tales in the Old French period, and it is used in the texts of a large number of works considered fabliaux today. In the Romantic era it was the fashion to use the word to characterize any short composition from the medieval period. Today, however, its application is more precise and closer to its original use, which was to designate a distinct genre.

The fabliau is descended from the fable of classical antiquity, and a comparison at several points with the older form will help to make clear its peculiar characteristics: (1) The fable, like the parable of the New Testament, is a tale with a moral purpose. The fabliau, on the other hand, exploits the story for its own sake, being intended solely to amuse the listener. Except for some very early examples, it illustrates no moral precept and has no didactic purpose whatsoever. It is, in fact, perhaps the first distinct genre in Western literature of which this may be said. (2) The fable traditionally uses animal characters. The fabliau, with few exceptions, is concerned with ordinary people. (3) The fable may be either in prose or verse. The fabliaux always are in verse, all but one in octosyllabic rhymed couplets. (4) The fable is serious in purpose, if not always in content. The most essential characteristic of the fabliau, on the other hand, is that it is always a humorous tale.

The fabliau is, in short, a brief tale in verse written to amuse, with characters, action, and scenes drawn from real life, and with few supernatural or marvelous elements. Or, in the even more succinct definition of the medievalist Joseph Bédier, it is *un conte à rire en vers.*

In surviving manuscript compilations from the thirteenth and fourteenth centuries, there are 160 tales that merit the title of fabliau, according to the criteria recently laid down by the scholar Per Nykrog. They were composed between the last years of the twelfth century and 1346, the year in which Jean de Condé, the last author to exploit the form, died. The conditions that produced and propagated the fabliaux are imperfectly understood, but, after their first appearance, they spread rapidly and with remarkable vitality throughout Northern France, particularly in the region of Paris and in the provinces of Picardy, Flanders, and Normandy.

It was the fashion among scholars of the last generation to divide the vernacular literature of medieval France into two categories, courtly and bourgeois, and to attribute the origin of the latter, in which the fabliaux occupy an important position, to the rise of the prosperous towns and commercial centers of northern France, where the newly affluent middle class demanded a literature whose spirit would reflect the workaday life and ideals of the burghers and merchants more accurately than did the courtly romances with their formal allegory and their idealized knights and ladies. Today, however, students of Old French literature are more likely to regard the so-called bourgeois literature as a development of the courtly tradition, and to see in it a reaction which tended to parody the prevailing mode of fabulous romance.

Many of the fabliaux do parody traditional situations in the courtly romances. For example, the love sickness of the courtly hero is gently burlesqued in "William of the Falcon." But the parodic intention of the fabliaux is most apparent in their mock-heroic imitation of the style of the romances or epics. In "The Lay of Aristotle," for example, the grave tone of the opening lines stands in marked contrast to the comic treatment of Aristotle's wisdom and infatuation. Similarly, a fabliau by Gautier le Leu, "Conebert" (not included in this collection), uses an epic style to relate an obscenely comic story.

This deliberate discrepancy between style and subject matter would seem to indicate that the audience of the fabliaux had a certain sophistication and some familiarity with the tenets of courtly love. The fabliaux, in other words, could not have been written for an exclusively middle-class audience.

But it would be wrong to impose on the fabliaux as a genre a strict unity of conception and purpose, and it would be as misleading to attribute to all the tales an aristocratic point of view as to assume that they were all bound by middle-class attitudes. The subject matter, purpose, and tone of the fabliaux that have been preserved are enormously at variance. They represent the product of many authors, known and anonymous, of various social classes and situations. And they span four or five generations which witnessed profound social, economic, and literary changes. Some of the fabliaux are comprehensible only from the vantage point of the aristocracy, others from that of the merchant class. Two distinct versions of "Beranger Longbottom" survive, one of which systematically eliminates the element of class satire found in the original, courtly version translated here. This suggests the possibility that it was rewritten for an audience which might take offense at the element of class spite. It is clear that the fabliaux cannot be assigned to a single social milieu. Rather, the courtly literature, the heroic poem, and the fabliau are three manifestations of the same spirit and age.

Composed for and enjoyed by all social classes, the fabliaux were recited or read at every occasion which brought people together: in the courts of France and England, both great and small; in the taverns of the bustling cities and commercial centers; in the homes of the prosperous burghers of the town and of the country squires, both of whom were eager to imitate the style of life of their betters. It is conceivable that fabliaux were told at formal ceremonies in court and castle as comic relief after the recitation of a battle epic or a chivalric romance. They may have been recited on the steps of a church or on a busy street corner at market time, or during one of the important fairs. They may even—God forbid—have been heard in the rectory or the cloister. The evidence suggests that some may have been composed for the guild hall, like that of the Confrérie de la Sainte Chandelle at Arras, to which the early author Jean Bodel belonged. Certainly they would have formed part of the entertainment on a voyage or pilgrimage, a situation familiar to readers of *The Canterbury Tales*. In short, the fabliaux were enjoyed on any occasion which called for laughter and an escape from daily routine.

Just as audiences for the fabliaux differed widely, so there are vast differences in the origins of the tales, in their length, their subject matter, their style, and in the quality of their humor. Some of the plots have a particularly close affinity with certain Indian and Arabic tales ("The Lay of Aristotle"), others with the collections from Greek and Roman antiquity (the retelling of Petronius' "Matron of Ephesus" in "The Woman Who Hanged Her Husband's Body"). Many, however, cannot be traced to a definite source, but seem to spring from very ancient and universal folk traditions ("The Partridges"), or perhaps from true events or local gossip transformed by the poet's imagination (Rutebeuf's "Brother Denise"). They vary a great deal in length; some consist of less than a hundred brief, eight-syllable lines and depend on a single unadorned anecdote—a long and, in some cases, dirty joke;[1] others require hundreds of lines to compose their numerous, intricately interwoven plot elements and characters into an elaborate tale.

Despite wide divergence of styles among the fabliaux, they have sufficient traits in common to permit some general observations. While many poets, like Henri d'Andeli in his prologue to "The Lay of Aristotle," denounce baseness of expression, *oevre ou vilanie cort,* and take considerable pains with matters of style, the majority of the tales are written in unpolished language—the "low style." The expression of most is deliberately popular, and in some cases crude. Colloquial idiom abounds, and there is a liberal use of well-known proverbs, of puns, and of familiar plays on words. The poets usually refrain from euphemisms, preferring to call a spade a spade; the abundance of "four-letter words" bears out Nykrog's statement that the audience "feared neither the word nor the thing it designated." But, in spite of their lack of artistic pretension, there is one strikingly consistent quality in these stories: a self-conscious style which deftly organizes the narrative elements to achieve the effect desired; the means are very effectively adapted to their ends. The authors of the fabliaux knew that to be funny a story must be well

[1] The shortest fabliau to come down to us, "The Priest and the Sheep," by Haiseau, requires no more than eighteen lines to tell its story: "A priest loved a lady who was wed to a knight. The priest kept a sheep in his house who was wont to butt people. One day, as the priest lay with the lady, the sheep saw the priest raise his head, and he took this as a sign to charge. He slipped up on the priest from behind and gave him such a painful blow on his tonsured head that he was quite stunned. And the lady had no pleasure that day, for the priest was in no condition to be of service to her; thus they had to leave off their sport. Haiseau wishes to teach by this tale that *one ought indeed keep his eyes open.*" (Montaiglon-Raynaud, VI, 50)

told; the laugh must come at the right place, and all elements of the narrative must be subordinated to this end. Digressions, intrusions on the part of the poet, descriptions, characterizations, all must be kept to a minimum so as not to hinder the movement of the action. In the words of R. C. Johnston, these poets "had the virtue of wasting no time in the telling of the tale, and their very artlessness means the absence of one barrier between us and the vigorous, colorful age which they reflect. Stylistic elegance would have been quite out of place in the majority of these tales."

The most important quality of the fabliau is its humor— sometimes silly and superficial, elsewhere introducing parody and satire or a broad and bawdy humor that is often mere slapstick—a humor at times morbid, as in "The Woman Who Hanged Her Husband's Body," cruel, as in "The Snow Baby," or grotesque, as in "The Knight Who Conjured Voices." More often than not the laugh was provoked at the expense of traditional morality (for example, in "The Wife of Orleans," where the wife is completely successful in her adulterous trick). One element of the comic lay in exploiting stock attitudes toward many of the characters, such as the scorn for women, priests, peasants, and boorish husbands. Like certain characters from Roman comedy or medieval farce, the peasant in "Brunain" had only to step on stage to be obviously funny. The humor is characteristic of the *esprit gaulois*, that spirit of broad gallic humor prevalent in French storytelling from the Middle Ages to the present day. It is a spirit fundamental to writers as different in inspiration and as far apart in time as Rabelais, La Fontaine, Balzac. And the fabliaux were the first sizable body of vernacular works to display this spirit. In its treatment of sex, a theme which is central to most of the fabliaux, this humor is coarse but without prurience or sensuality, and it manifests an ironic and mischievous attitude toward sacred and quasi-sacred ideas and institutions.

Although a few of the fabliaux, such as "The Butcher of Abbeville" and "The Knight Who Conjured Voices," show the beginnings of character development, the great majority dispense with characterization or even elementary psychological motivation. The psychology of the characters is not described, other than with a brief "and the lady loved a squire," or "the tavern keeper was haughty." The characters are stock figures or conventional types, most often barely individualized and without development. We must wait for Chaucer and Boccaccio to add the dimension of character to the fabliaux, although occasionally we do find remarkably individualized portraits, such as that of Gautier le Leu's "Widow."

These types, although they include some bishops and knights, are mostly of the third estate. There is the merchant, industrious, canny in business, and yet naïve where women are concerned; traditionally much older than his wife, he is invariably duped, cuckolded, robbed, and sometimes beaten into the bargain. There is the young lover, most often a squire or a young student—a "lusty bacheleer," as Chaucer was to call him—who does well with the wives and daughters and who generally wins out over his rivals, the lecherous clerics of the country parish or the monastery. The priests and the monks are treated in a consistently hostile fashion, and almost invariably turn out to be the losers in the contests with their rivals. It is the women who, reflecting the monkish attitude of the times, are the most consistently portrayed of the *dramatis personae*. They are, almost without exception, unscrupulous, lecherous, lustful, inconstant,

quarrelsome, gluttonous, shameless, and treacherous, and re-
sort to the most ingenious shifts and stratagems to deceive
their husbands or take revenge on them. As we read in "The
Wife of Orleans," "women, by their tricks, have deceived
men since the time of Abel"; even the wisest of mortals,
Solomon, fell victim to the deceitful charms of a woman,
and the image of Aristotle with a saddle on his back has
come down to posterity. How does one deal with such crea-
tures? "Beat their bones and break their backs!" the author
of one fabliau suggests. And unlike François Villon's women,
many of whom have some of the same vices, but who command our sympathy, the women of the fabliaux are treated
without compassion, as necessary evils who, left unguarded
for a moment, will bring shame on their husbands.

Besides these three figures of the eternal triangle, other
characters, no less colorful, fill the pages of the fabliaux.
There is the insufferable tavern keeper who spills wine on the
poor clerk; the trusting peasant who, out of charity (and
because she gives very little milk) offers his cow to God;
the crowd of ruffians in "The Wife of Orleans" who, seem-
ingly for pure pleasure and the promise of wine, beat a
stranger to a pulp. There are maidservants, altar boys, village
gossips, messengers, squires, thieves, kings, every conceivable
variety of monastic order and regular clergy, peasants, merchants, tradesmen, and a quack, with Alexander the Great,
Saint Martin, and some fairies thrown in for good measure.
The whole body of fabliaux, unlike any other early genre of
Old French literature, depicts a complete panorama of medieval society, teeming with life, color, movement—truly an
important source for our knowledge of the times.

If these personages are not profoundly characterized, they
are at least full of life, in the same manner as certain types

of the silent movie or the *commedia dell' arte*. They move against a vivid background of the daily life of court, town, and country: the market place, the fields and mills, the churches and cloisters, the chambers and hall of a castle, the gardens, the taverns, the tournaments. But the most important setting for the action of the fabliaux is the domestic interior. In most of the fabliaux, of course, it is in the bedroom with its curtained bed that the most important action takes place. But there are also the kitchen and the hall, warm and cozy, full of the smells of roasting fowl and mutton, of good wine, and of cakes and sweetmeats.

But the fabliards do not dwell on the details of their settings; all the poet allows himself is a quick epithet, a very brief description or an apology for the lack of one. In the best of the tales this cursory treatment is enough to provide a sense of place: a garden behind a locked gate, a house with a high window, a country that consists only of a high hill and a hot sun. The descriptions are more circumstantial than evocative and never so long or detailed as to divert the audience's attention from the action to the scenery.

The fabliaux are, of course, written in verse. It is not very great verse perhaps, in some cases little more than doggerel; yet it is remarkably well suited to its purpose. The eight-syllable rhymed couplets are fluent and fast, never hindering the narrative, which rolls along at great speed to its denouement. The narrative is filled out with lively dialogue that is always terse and sometimes witty, abounding in colloquial and colorful expressions, occasionally imitating local speech habits and locutions, or even foreign accents, and so imparting a racy, realistic quality to the tale which is altogether missing from the courtly romances and from the various moral and didactic stories of the period. The fabliau is the first major genre to employ dialogue so extensively and to such good effect. As much as sixty percent of a tale may be devoted to direct discourse; and the dialogue gives a sense of character at the same time that it advances the action of the story. Note, for example, the swift-moving and realistic conversation between the priest, the lady and the servant in "The Butcher of Abbeville."

Just as there was a broad diversity of social milieus which took pleasure in the fabliaux, so the situations of the poet-minstrels differed widely, from the most wretched hack performer, reciting corrupt and gratuitously scabrous versions of tales composed by more subtle minds, to the polished poet, well-bred, highly conscious of his art, and adept at achieving the effects he desired. Most of the fabliaux remain anonymous, but a sufficient number of authors are known to give us an idea of the manner of life they led.

Although among these poets we find an important ecclesiastic, Henri d'Andeli, and a knight in the person of Philippe de Beaumanoir, Lord of Clermont, most of the authors were professional entertainers. An important and colorful group was the wandering students. Ecclesiastics in minor orders, errant monks, perhaps even unfrocked priests, all destitute followers of "Bishop Golias," they swarmed in the university towns of Paris and Orleans, quarreling, drinking, begging, and composing and reciting their tales to eke out a rather miserable existence. Burghers and powerful ecclesiastics, even the nobility, would receive them into their houses, where the poets recited their tales in exchange for a meal or a gown, as shown in "The Poor Student," translated here, or in the following passage from the prologue to "The Sacristan": "It is the custom in Normandy that a person who is lodged tell a fabliau or sing a song to his host, and Jean le Chapelain will abide by this custom." The fabliaux composed by this group are most often anonymous, but the sympathetic treatment of the impecunious cleric or student, as in "The Miller and the Two Clerics" or "The Wife of Orleans," suggests that members of this class were indeed the authors. They are, in fact, the only class of people in the tales who are not roughly handled by the poets.

Although they were poverty-stricken and led precarious lives, these goliards had received a good education in the schools and were protected by ecclesiastical law. Perhaps they had failed to receive their benefice, or they may have been forced to leave their studies for lack of money (*see* "The Poor Student"); more likely, they had been seduced by the temptations of "dice, women, and the tavern." It is easy to see why these declassed wanderers should despise the industry of the burgher and the dullness of the villain and envy the respectability and relative prosperity of the regular and monastic clergy. Their attitude toward women was the conventional clerical one toward the daughters of Eve: cynicism, reinforced perhaps by the notion they had of themselves as irresistible seducers of womankind.

The largest class of poets who wrote fabliaux were the jongleurs. The names of about twenty of these are known, for professional pride led them to sign their works. About most of them we know very little, except perhaps that they were poor, like the wandering scholars. The works of some, such as Rutebeuf, provide us with a wealth of information about their lives and characters. Some had unusual names like Rutebeuf or Courtebarbe, others aristocratic-sounding ones like Enguerrand d'Oisi or Eustache d'Amiens, while most were nondescript like Garin, Durand, or Guillaume. The texts reveal that, in general, their lives were even more disreputable than those of the students; they enjoyed little or no status in society and were despised by the merchant class, the nobility, and the intellectuals alike. Wandering from fair to castle to tavern, a motley crew, *plebs sine nomine,* they drank up or diced away their meager earnings and, like François Villon two hundred years later, were often forced to leave behind their cloak or books as security for the wine they drank. But there were a few jongleurs who, though hardly rich, led a more regular life and enjoyed the esteem of their contemporaries; such were Jean Bodel, who lived among the burghers of Arras, and Rutebeuf, who was associated with the intellectuals of Paris.

Finally, there was a small group of authors who flourished in the early fourteenth century—the minstrels, like Jean de Condé or Jacques de Baisieux, who were attached to courts and had official status, writing and performing for the edification or amusement of their patrons.

The fabliaux were a source of inspiration and of plots, not only for writers who came immediately after the period in which they were composed, but also for those in the centuries following, right into the nineteenth century, when Balzac wrote his archaizing work, *Contes Drolatiques.* The two greatest storytellers of the Middle Ages borrowed freely from the fabliaux, Boccaccio in the *Decameron* and Chaucer in *The Canterbury Tales.* The story of "The Miller and the Two Clerics" in this collection is almost identical in plot to Chaucer's "Reeve's Tale"; other stories in *The Canterbury Tales* which derive from the fabliaux are the "Miller's Tale" and the "Summoner's Tale." In France the fabliau had run its course as an independent genre by the second half of the fourteenth century; but fabliau themes and motifs were reworked and adapted in farces, in serious collections like *Le*

Livre du Chevalier de la Tour Landry (1371), in thirteenth-
century collections of *exempla,* such as those of Jacques de
Vitry and Etienne de Bourbon, and in satirical works like
the *Fifteen Joys of Marriage* (*ca.* 1400). We find the familiar
stories in collections of tales modeled on those of Boccaccio,
like the *Cent Nouvelles Nouvelles* (*Hundred New Tales;*
1462) of the Burgundian court, the tales of Philippe de Vig-
neulles (early sixteenth century) and Bonaventure des Périers
(1510–1544), and the *Heptameron* (pub. 1558) of Marguerite
de Navarre, sister of Francis I. In the seventeenth century
many of the tales of Boccaccio find a new and elegant form
in the *Contes et Nouvelles* of La Fontaine.

In English there are extant early translations of three fabliaux. Fabliau themes found their way, through popular
jestbooks like *A Hundred Merry Tales* (1526), into the
Elizabethan theater. The fabliaux were reworked in Catalan,
in such works as the *Castia Gilos* of Raimon Vidal de Bezalu
(first half of the thirteenth century); in German, notably by
Hans Sachs and in the nineteenth-century collection of
medieval tales, the *Gesammtabenteuer,* by Friedrich Heinrich
von de Hagen; in Italian, by Poggio (1380–1459), Malespini
(second half of the sixteenth century), Basile (1575–1632),
and by scores of others; in Spanish, in *The Book of Good
Love* (1330) by Juan Ruiz, Archpriest of Hita, and in other
Spanish collections dealing with the wiles of women. There
are several collections in Flemish and Dutch, and fabliau
themes have passed into such works as *Till Eulenspiegel* and
the *Adages* (1505) of Erasmus. There is even a nineteenth-
century Russian collection, *The Secret Tales,* which preserves
some of the fabliau motifs.

BIBLIOGRAPHICAL NOTE

The great majority of the texts of the fabliaux, in the original Old French, are available in:

Anatole de Montaiglon and Gaston Raynaud. *Recueil général et complet des fabliaux des XIIIe et XIVe siècles.* 6 vols. Paris: Librairie des Bibliophiles, 1872–1890.

Two recent publications contain editions of twenty-four fabliaux with introduction, notes, and glossary in English:

R. C. Johnston and D. D. R. Owen. *Fabliaux.* Oxford: Blackwell, 1957.

T. B. W. Reid. *Twelve Fabliaux from MS F. Fr. 19152 of the Bibliothèque Nationale.* Manchester: Manchester University Press, 1958.

Of the numerous studies devoted to the fabliaux the following are the most important:

Joseph Bédier. *Les Fabliaux: Etudes de littérature populaire et d'histoire littéraire du moyen âge.* Paris: Champion, 1925.

Per Nykrog. *Les Fabliaux: Etude d'histoire littéraire et de stylistique médiévale.* Copenhagen: Munksgaard, 1957.

Jean Rychner. *Contribution à l'étude des fabliaux.* 2 vols. Geneva: Droz, 1960.

The work by Nykrog contains an extensive bibliography for the reader who may wish to go deeper into the literature on the fabliaux. Two of the most important manuscripts which preserve the texts of the fabliaux have been published in facsimile editions:

Edmond Faral. *Le Manuscrit 19152 du fonds français de la Bibliothèque Nationale*. Paris, 1934.

Henri Omont. *Fabliaux, Dits et contes en vers français du XIIIe siècle*. Paris, 1932.